Biological Oscillators:

Their Mathematical Analysis

Biological Oscillators: Their Mathematical Analysis

THEODOSIOS PAVLIDIS

Department of Electrical Engineering
Princeton University
Princeton, New Jersey

ACADEMIC PRESS   New York and London   1973

A Subsidiary of Harcourt Brace Jovanovich, Publishers

ACADEMIC PRESS, INC.
111 Fifth Avenue, New York, New York 10003

United Kingdom Edition published by
ACADEMIC PRESS, INC. (LONDON) LTD.
24/28 Oval Road, London NW1

Library of Congress Cataloging in Publication Data

Pavlidis, Theodosios.
    Biological oscillators.

    Bibliography: p.
        1.   Biology—Periodicity.   2.   Biological control
systems—Mathematical models.   3.   Oscillations.
I.   Title.
QH527.P38   574.1   72-13615
ISBN 0–12–547350–8

Dedicated to the memory of my father
P A U L

Contents

Chapter 1. Fundamentals of the Mathematical Theory of Oscillators

Chapter 2. Examples of Biological Rhythms

Chapter 3. Phase Shifts and Phase Response Curves

Chapter 8. **Biological Phenomena Attributable to Populations of Oscillators**

Preface

The goal of this monograph is to present the main features of the dynamic properties of biological oscillators and the mathematical techniques necessary for their investigation. It is not a comprehensive description of all known biological oscillators, since this would require a much bigger volume as well as a different type of expertise. Certain classes of biological oscillators are described and then only in as much detail as is required for the study of their dynamics.

Biological oscillators present a host of problems which are peculiar to them. Whereas in most technical applications the important variables and equations of the system are well known, this is rarely, if ever, the case in biological systems. Thus one must use indirect means for their description. In many instances the usual problems are placed in a converse form. In technological applications one usually starts with the structural description of a system and then determines its behavior during, say, nonlinear resonance (entrainment). In a biological system one attempts to deduce its structure from experimentally obtained behavior. In other cases the whole problem might be peculiar to living systems. For example, there is strong evidence that many biological clocks consist of a population of mutually coupled oscillators. There are very few other applications where one deals with more than two or three coupled oscillators. This fact together with the intrinsic mathematical difficulty of the problem can explain the scarcity of the technical literature about such systems.

The analysis of the various techniques emphasizes the use of mathematics as tools and it does not include rigorous proofs. A number of mathematical models of specific biological systems are presented together with results of computer simulations. Hopefully this will make the treatment accessible to anyone familiar with the basic concepts and the formalism of elementary differential equations and linear algebra.

Most of the examples and many of the general questions discussed are from the area of low frequency biological rhythms reflecting my own personal interest in that subject.

Acknowledgments

I owe much to Colin S. Pittendrigh, now at Stanford University, who introduced me to the subject and helped me to start my research in this area. He has continued to be a constant inspiration in my work on biological rhythms. I also wish to thank his former students and associates at Princeton and, in particular, William F. Zimmerman, Arthur T. Winfree, and Victor G. Bruce for the many discussions I have had with them while developing the ideas which eventually resulted in this monograph. In this book I have used many examples from the literature and have included descriptions of experimental results in order to illustrate the various mathematical techniques discussed. I am grateful to J. A. Bourret (California State University, Long Beach), Britton Chance and E. Kendall Pye (University of Pennsylvania), Patricia DeCoursey (University of South Carolina), Jerry F. Feldman, Ruth Halaban, and Jon W. Jacklet (State University of New York, Albany), Klaus Hoffmann (Max-Planck-Institut für Verhaltenphysiologie), S. Jerebzoff (Universite Paul Sabatier, Toulouse, France), Colin S. Pittendrigh (Stanford University), Shepherd K. Roberts (Temple University), Richard H. Swade (San Fernando Valley State College, Northridge, California), and Arthur T. Winfree (Purdue University) for permitting me to reproduce figures and tables from their papers. I am thankful to Mrs. Pearl Bazel for her excellent typing of the manuscript and to Steven L. Horowitz for his help in some of the computer simulations. Last but not least I want to express my gratitude to my wife Marian and my children Paul, Karen, and Harry for their patience and understanding while this book was completed.

CHAPTER 1

Fundamentals of the Mathematical Theory of Oscillators

1.1 Introduction

This chapter contains a review of fundamental mathematical concepts and techniques which will be used in the remainder of the book. Most of this material is covered in courses on feedback theory and/or nonlinear systems of senior or first-year graduate level. Thus readers with strong technical backgrounds could skip this chapter. Others may find it necessary to read selected sections. The background necessary for its comprehension is calculus plus elementary linear algebra. This material is usually covered in the first two years of college courses. Since an increasing number of biologists attend such courses we felt that it was safe to assume it as reasonable background for the book.

The next two sections deal with the phase plane techniques, including an example from the theory of population dynamics. The fourth section points out the salient features of the study of n-dimensional dynamical systems. Next the asymptotic techniques of Krylov, Bogoliubov, and Mitopolski are presented. These are based in approximating nonlinear systems by linear ones. The sixth section deals with another linearization technique, that of the describing function. Finally we review briefly certain aspects of conservative systems, a class which can be handled analytically easier than others and for this reason is often discussed in the literature.

A number of references are listed for further reading at the end of each section. The following are some which we found particularly useful for an overall treatment of nonlinear oscillations: And-I (comprehensive), Bog-I, But-I, Dav-I (concise with many specific examples), Haa-I, Haj-I, Hal-I (rigorous and concise), Hay-I (many examples), Lef-I, Lef-II, Min-I (comprehensive), Min-II, Nem-I (abstract treatment), Oga-I, Oga-II, Pli-I, Saa-I, San-I, Ura-I.

1.2   Phase Plane Techniques

The dynamic behavior of many physical systems can often be described by a second-order differential equation or a system of two first-order differential equations. Such descriptions involve two variables, which if known at any given time t_0 allow the prediction of the behavior of the system for any time $t > t_0$ on the basis of the solution of the differential equation(s). For example, the position $p(t_0)$ and velocity $v(t_0)$ of a mass m suspended from a spring with constant k determine its further motion on the basis of the equation

$$m \, d^2p/dt^2 + kp = 0 \tag{1.2.1}$$

Indeed the solution to the above is

$$p(t) = A \cos[(k/m)^{1/2} \cdot t + \phi] \tag{1.2.2}$$

for some constants A and ϕ. These can be determined uniquely from the conditions

$$p(t_0) = A \cos \phi, \qquad v(t_0) = -(k/m)^{1/2} A \sin \phi \tag{1.2.3}$$

The two variables which characterize the behavior of the system are usually called the *state* of the system. They can be represented as coordinates in a plane and in this way the behavior of the systems can be described in terms of plane curves. Thus the derivative of Eq. (1.2.2) is

$$v(t) = -(k/m)^{1/2} A \sin[(k/m)^{1/2} t + \phi] \tag{1.2.4}$$

Eliminating the time-dependent terms between this equation and Eq. (1.2.1) we obtain

$$p^2 + (m/k) v^2 = A^2 \tag{1.2.5}$$

which represents an ellipse in the plane with coordinates p and v. The curves which result by eliminating the time from the solution of the differential equation(s) are called the *trajectories* of the system and the plane where they are plotted the *phase plane*.

This formalism is useful not so much in cases where the differential equation(s) can be solved explicitly as where they cannot. There exist graphoanalytical techniques which allow one to determine the trajectories or certain properties of them and in turn deduce the dynamic behavior of the system. We will study some of these techniques next.

The general form of the mathematical equations describing a system which can be studied on the phase plane with (x, y) coordinates is

$$S: \begin{cases} dx/dt = f(x, y) & (1.2.6) \\ dy/dt = g(x, y) & (1.2.7) \end{cases}$$

Such a system is often called *one degree of freedom* because its motion is along a plane curve. This term, unfortunately, is often misunderstood to imply that the dynamic behavior of the system can be described by a single variable, which is certainly not true. Another common term is *second-order system*, which does not leave room for misunderstanding and which has been motivated by the fact that in general any system of the form given by Eqs. (1.2.6) and (1.2.7) is equivalent to one described by a single second-order differential equation.

Any such equation can be placed in the above form. Indeed consider the following:

$$d^2x/dt^2 + f(x, dx/dt) = 0 \qquad (1.2.8)$$

This is obviously equivalent to

$$dx/dt = y \qquad (1.2.9)$$

$$dy/dt = -f(x, y) \qquad (1.2.10)$$

The converse is also usually true. If $f(x, y)$ is differentiable with respect to both of its arguments, then differentiating Eq. (1.2.6) with respect to time we obtain

$$\frac{d^2x}{dt^2} = \frac{\partial f}{\partial x}\frac{dx}{dt} + \frac{\partial f}{\partial y}\frac{dy}{dt}$$

or

$$\frac{d^2x}{dt^2} - \frac{\partial f}{\partial x}\frac{dx}{dt} - \frac{\partial f}{\partial y}g(x, y) = 0 \qquad (1.2.11)$$

If Eq. (1.2.6) can be solved with respect to y, then an expression of the form

$$y = F(x, dx/dt)$$

is obtained. Substituting this for y in Eq. (1.2.11) leaves an equation in x, dx/dt, and d^2x/dt^2. Although these transformations (differentiation and solution with respect to y) are not always possible, they are valid in most cases of practical interest. A similar reasoning can be used to obtain a second-order differential equation with respect to y.

The points (x_e, y_e) for which the functions $f(x, y)$ and $g(x, y)$ take the value zero are called *points of equilibrium* or *singularities* or *critical points* of the system S. If the initial values of (x, y) are equal to the coordinates of such a point then they will remain the same since both derivatives dx/dt and dy/dt are zero.

What will happen if the point (x, y) is close but not exactly equal to a point of equilibrium? Obviously there are only three possibilities:

(1)   The distance between (x, y) and (x_e, y_e) increases with time. Then the point (x_e, y_e) is called *unstable*.
(2)   The distance decreases with time; (x_e, y_e) is called *asymptotically stable*.
(3)   The distance varies with time but it stays between an upper and a lower bound; (x_e, y_e) is called *neutrally stable*.

In (1) and (2) the changes are not necessarily monotonic.

We can study the type of stability in the proximity of an equilibrium point by using a linearization of Eqs. (1.2.6) and (1.2.7). Let

$$x = x_e + \xi, \qquad y = y_e + \eta$$

Then substituting these quantities in the above equations and using a Taylor series expansion for $f(x, y)$ and $g(x, y)$ we obtain

$$\frac{d\xi}{dt} = f(x_e, y_e) + \frac{\partial f}{\partial x}\xi + \frac{\partial g}{\partial y}\eta + \frac{\partial^2 f}{\partial x^2}\xi^2 + 2\frac{\partial^2 f}{\partial x\,\partial y}\xi\eta + \frac{\partial^2 f}{\partial y^2}\eta^2 + \cdots$$

$$\frac{d\eta}{dt} = g(x_e, y_e) + \frac{\partial g}{\partial x}\xi + \frac{\partial g}{\partial y}\eta + \frac{\partial^2 g}{\partial x^2}\xi^2 + 2\frac{\partial^2 g}{\partial x\,\partial y}\xi\eta + \frac{\partial^2 g}{\partial y^2}\eta^2 + \cdots$$

The partial derivatives are all computed at the point (x_e, y_e). The first term of each expansion is by definition equal to zero. For sufficiently small ξ and η the higher terms can be eliminated and we thus have

$$d\xi/dt = f_x \cdot \xi + f_y \cdot \eta \tag{1.2.12}$$

$$d\eta/dt = g_x \cdot \xi + g_y \cdot \eta \tag{1.2.13}$$

where f_x stands for $\partial f/\partial x$, etc.

This is a linear system and it can easily be transformed into an equation of the form

$$d^2\xi/dt^2 - (f_x + g_y)\,d\xi/dt + (f_x g_y - g_x f_y)\xi = 0 \tag{1.2.14}$$

An identical equation can be obtained with respect to η.

The solution of this differential equation is of the form

$$\xi = A\,e^{\lambda_1 t} + B\,e^{\lambda_2 t} \tag{1.2.15}$$

where A and B depend on the initial conditions and λ_1, λ_2 are the two roots of the algebraic equation

$$\lambda^2 - (f_x + g_y)\lambda + (f_x g_y - g_x f_y) = 0 \tag{1.2.16}$$

The solution for η is obtained by substituting Eq. (1.2.15) into (1.2.12):

$$\eta = \frac{\lambda_1 - f_x}{f_y}\,A\,e^{\lambda_1 t} + \frac{\lambda_2 - f_x}{f_y}\,B\,e^{\lambda_2 t} \tag{1.2.17}$$

If one or both of the λ_1 and λ_2 have *positive real parts*, then ξ and η will increase with time and the point (x_e, y_e) will be *unstable*.

If both λ_1 and λ_2 have *negative real parts*, then ξ and η will tend to zero and the point will be *asymptotically stable*.

If both λ_1 and λ_2 have zero real parts or one has zero and the other a negative real part, the point will be *neutrally stable*.

Note that the sum of the real parts of λ_1 and λ_2 is $f_x + g_y$ and thus an obvious *necessary* condition for stability is

$$f_x + g_y < 0 \tag{1.2.18}$$

The product $\lambda_1\lambda_2$ equals $f_x g_y - g_x f_y$. For stability it is *necessary* that both roots have the same sign or that

$$f_x g_y - g_x f_y > 0 \tag{1.2.19}$$

It is easy to verify that (1.2.18) and (1.2.19) *together* are *sufficient* conditions for the stability of x_e, y_e.

We may further verify that the roots will be real if

$$(f_x + g_y)^2 - 4(f_x g_y - g_x f_y) > 0$$

or

$$(f_x - g_y)^2 + 4g_x f_y > 0 \tag{1.2.20}$$

This analysis allows us to plot the trajectories of the system in the neighborhood of an equilibrium point (see Fig. 1.2.1). Table 1.2.1 is a list of the various types of possible configurations encountered together with their usual nomenclature.

The behavior of the system away from an equilibrium point is more difficult to study.

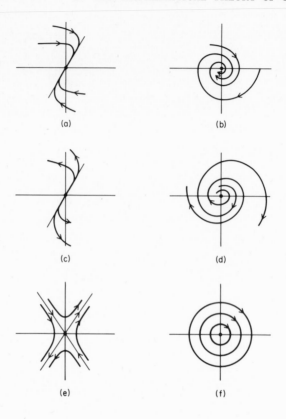

FIG. 1.2.1.   Phase plane portraits in the neighborhood of various types of singularities (see text for further explanations; also see Table 1.2.1).

TABLE 1.2.1

| | Sign of quantity in inequality | | | |
Name	1.2.18	1.2.19	1.2.20	Part of Fig. 1.2.1
Stable node	−	+	+	a
Stable focus	−	+	−	b
Unstable node	+	+	+	c
Unstable focus	+	+	−	d
Saddle point	+	−	+	e
Saddle point	−	−	+	e
Center	0	+	−	f

There is an interesting set of trajectories which close in themselves and correspond to periodic oscillatory motion. These can be called *periodic trajectories* and are of obvious relevance to the subject of this book. They share with points of equilibrium the property that once the state of the system is in them it will remain there for all times. The name *invariant sets* is applicable to both points of equilibrium and periodic trajectories. The notion of stability is also applicable to the latter with the obvious specification. The only additional complication occurs because of the division of the phase plane into two parts by such a trajectory: inside and outside. Thus one can have stability from the outside and instability from the inside (Fig. 1.2.2).

Fig. 1.2.2. A periodic trajectory which is stable from the outside but unstable from the inside.

Periodic trajectories which are *asymptotically stable* from both sides are called *stable limit cycles* or simply *limit cycles*. Those which are *unstable* from both sides are called *unstable limit cycles* or *antilimit cycles*.

Poincaré studied various properties of periodic trajectories using the concept of the *index*. A full description of his analysis is outside the scope of this brief review, but the following is a summary of his results:

(1) A periodic trajectory must surround at least one point of equilibrium.

(2) If it surrounds exactly one point, then this cannot be a saddle point; i.e., condition (1.2.19) must be satisfied at this point.

(3) If it surrounds more than one point, then there should be exactly one more focus, node, or center than saddle points.

Additional results about such trajectories have been obtained by a number of investigators, including Bendixon, Andronov, and others. Thus the above list can be supplemented by the following:

(4) If the expression

$$f_x + g_y$$

does not change sign (or vanish identically) within a region D of the phase plane, then no periodic trajectories exist in D.

(5) If a trajectory remains in a finite domain D for $t > 0$ and it does not approach any points of equilibrium, then either it is a

periodic trajectory or it approaches such a trajectory. (This is known as the *Poincaré-Bendixon theorem*.)

(6)   If a finite set of periodic trajectories are nested (as in Fig. 1.2.3), then stable ones must alternate with unstable (the configuration of Fig. 1.2.3 is typical).

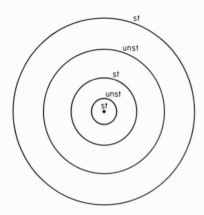

FIG. 1.2.3. A set of nested periodic trajectories. Stable ones alternate with unstable.

(7)   If a stable limit cycle encloses no other periodic trajectories, then it must enclose one unstable point of equilibrium. An unstable limit cycle must enclose one stable point of equilibrium.

The set of points from which all originating trajectories tend to a given stable limit cycle L or a point of equilibrium E is called the *region of attraction* of L (or E). The boundary of such a region is called a *separatrix*. (Note that in Fig. 1.2.3 both unstable limit cycles are separatrices.)

The above results can help considerably in the analysis of the system S, but they are not sufficient. It is always necessary to add numerical or graphical analysis in order to obtain a precise picture of the dynamic behavior of the system. Computer simulation is an obvious aid. Among the graphical techniques the best known is the method of the *isoclines*. This is based on the observation that the slope of the trajectory dy/dx is given by the quantity

$$s = g(x, y)/f(x, y) \tag{1.2.21}$$

For a given value of s, Eq. (1.2.21) represents an algebraic curve which can be readily plotted. By filling the plane with such curves one forms a fairly good idea about the dynamics of the system S.

We will illustrate the concepts of the present discussion by a detailed example in the next section.

Bibliographical Note. Most of the material of this section can be found in virtually any book on nonlinear systems, oscillations [And-I], feedback control [Oga-II], etc. A classical reference is the book by Minorsky [Min-I]. The work by Lefschetz [Lef-I] contains a very thorough and rigorous discussion of Poincaré's Index.

1.3 An Example of Application of Phase Plane Techniques

About forty years ago Volterra described a mathematical model for the interaction between a prey and a predator. Under certain simplifying assumptions the dynamics of the two populations can be described by the following set of equations:

$$dx/dt = (ay - b)x \qquad (1.3.1)$$

$$dy/dt = (c - dx)y \qquad (1.3.2)$$

where x is the population of the predator, y that of the prey, and a, b, c, and d are constants [Vol-A, Min-I]. This system has been analyzed extensively in the literature [Vol-A, Min-I]. In many respects its behavior contradicts what it known about population dynamics and a number of investigators have come up with modifications of it. We will study such a model here in order to illustrate the application of phase plane techniques. This example was motivated by the work of Rosenwing and MacArthur [Ros-1]. It is obtained by replacing Eq. (1.3.2) by

$$dy/dt = [c - dx - h(y - p)^2]y \qquad (1.3.3)$$

The added term reflects the effects of overcrowding and difficulty of reproduction in small populations.

We find that x is constant $(dx/dt = 0)$ for

$$x = 0 \qquad (1.3.4)$$

or

$$y = b/a \qquad (1.3.5)$$

and that y is constant $(dy/dt = 0)$ for

$$y = 0 \qquad (1.3.6)$$

or

$$x = (1/d)[c - h(y - p)^2] \qquad (1.3.7)$$

These curves are isoclines and are shown in Fig. 1.3.1 under the

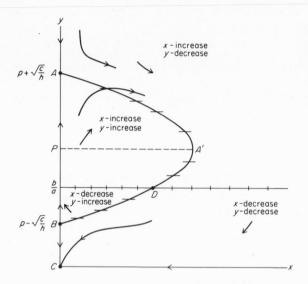

FIG. 1.3.1.   Phase plane portrait of Eqs. (1.3.1) and (1.3.3).

following assumptions:

$$0 < p - \sqrt{c}/h < b/a < p + \sqrt{c}/h \qquad (1.3.8)$$

$$b/a < p \qquad (1.3.9)$$

The first set of inequalities is required in order that the model agrees with certain obvious constraints resulting from population dynamics [Mac-1, Ros-1]. Their validity will be assumed throughout the subsequent development. Equation (1.3.9) does not have an obvious physical meaning and it will be discussed later.

The two axes constitute obviously trajectories and this guarantees that any motion starting in the first quadrant ($x \geqslant 0$ and $y \geqslant 0$) will stay there (trajectories cannot cross).

The pairwise intersections between the first two of these curves with the other two give the points of equilibrium. There are four of them in the first quadrant.

Table 1.3.1 summarizes their characteristics. D is stable if it occurs in the upper branch of the parabola and unstable in the lower branch. It is a center when $p = b/a$. When it is stable the steady state of the system will depend on the initial conditions. For some the final state will be at C and for others at D. A *separatrix* will divide the phase plane into two parts. This will be the trajectory leading into the saddle point B (Fig. 1.3.1) extending to infinity. A nonunique final state will

TABLE 1.3.1

CHARACTERISTIC OF THE SINGULARITIES OF THE SYSTEM OF EQS. (1.3.1) AND (1.3.3)[a]

	x	y	f_x	g_y	f_y	g_x	Sign of			Type
							S	T[b]	V	
A	0	$p + \dfrac{\sqrt{c}}{h}$	$(ap - b) + a\dfrac{\sqrt{c}}{h}$	$-2(ch)^{1/2}\left(p + \dfrac{\sqrt{c}}{h}\right)$	0	$-d\left(p + \dfrac{\sqrt{c}}{h}\right)$	?	−	+	Saddle point
B	0	$p - \dfrac{\sqrt{c}}{h}$	$(ap - b) - a\dfrac{\sqrt{c}}{h}$	$2(ch)^{1/2}\left(p - \dfrac{\sqrt{c}}{h}\right)$	0	$-d\left(p - \dfrac{\sqrt{c}}{h}\right)$	?	−	+	Saddle point
C	0	0	$-b$	$c - hp^2$	0	0	−	+	+	Stable node
							+[c]	+	+[d]	Stable node
							+[c]	+	−[d]	Stable focus
D	$\dfrac{1}{d}\left[c - h\left(p - \dfrac{b}{a}\right)^2\right]$	$\dfrac{b}{a}$	0	$\dfrac{2hb}{a}\left(p - \dfrac{b}{a}\right)$	$\dfrac{a}{d}\left[c - h\left(p - \dfrac{b}{a}\right)^2\right]$	$-\dfrac{db}{a}$	−[c]	+	−[d]	Unstable focus
							+[c]	+	+[d]	Unstable node

[a] $f_x = ay - b$, $f_y = ax$; $g_x = c - dx - h(3y - p)(y - p)$, $g_y = -dy$; $S = f_x + f_y$, $T = f_x g_y - f_y g_x$, $V = S^2 - 4T$.

[b] Because of Eq. (1.3.8).

[c] In this case S has the sign of $(p - b/a)$.

[d] In this case V has the sign of $(p - b/a)^2 - (c/h)a^2/(a^2 + hb)$; i.e., it is negative if $p - a/(a^2 + hb)^{1/2}\sqrt{c/h} < b/a < p + a/(a^2 + hb)^{1/2}\sqrt{c/h}$.

also exist if D is surrounded by a stable limit cycle. A detailed study of the isoclines around the point D can be used to investigate the question of its existence. An alternative way is to use computer simulation and plot a few trajectories starting near D. Both methods are essentially the same in that they require the numerical calculation of the right-hand sides of Eqs. (1.3.1) and (1.3.3) at a large number of points. Such an investigation reveals periodic trajectories only for values of b/a close to p.

An even more complex system results if we consider the effects of overpopulation on the predator. This can be done by replacing Eq. (1.3.1) with

$$dx/dt = (ay - b - kx^2)x \tag{1.3.10}$$

Then the characteristics of the points of equilibrium A, B, and C remain the same while certain changes occur in D. The dividing point between stable and unstable focus is not any more the tip of the parabola but some other point located in the lower arc. Furthermore a stable limit cycle is more likely to occur than before. Figure 1.3.2 illustrates

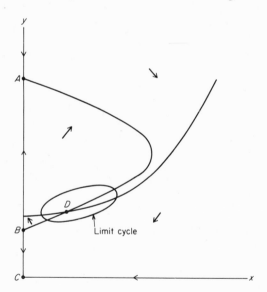

FIG. 1.3.2.   Phase plane portrait of Eqs. (1.3.10) and (1.3.3).

such a situation. The "upward bend" of the second parabola "stabilizes" the trajectories around an unstable focus.

Bibliographical Note.   This is only one example of extensive studies in the field of mathematical ecology. The reader can find in the literature additional examples of oscillatory as well as nonoscillatory systems [Ger-A, Ger-B, Goe-A, Lan-1, Lot-A, Mac-A, May-A, Pie-A]. A recent discussion of limit cycles in predator–prey systems can be found in the literature [May-1, Gil-1, and Ros-2].

1.4 State Space

The notion of the phase plane can be generalized for systems of more general form and in particular of the following:

$$S: dx/dt = f(x, t) \tag{1.4.1}$$

where x is an n-dimensional vector $(x_1, x_2, ..., x_n)$ and f a vector-valued function of $n + 1$ variables. The space of all such vectors is the *state space* of S and x is the state of the system.

The points of equilibrium x_e are defined by the condition

$$f(x_e, t) = 0 \quad \text{for all} \quad t \tag{1.4.2}$$

If t does not appear explicitly, then S is called an *autonomous* system. Let $J(x)$ be the Jacobian matrix of $f(x)$, namely the one which has the partial derivative

$$\partial f_i / \partial x_j$$

in its ith row and jth column. Then the linearized form of S is given by:

$$dx/dt = J(x_e)(x - x_e) \tag{1.4.3}$$

in the neighborhood of x_e. This state will be *asymptotically stable* if all the *eigenvalues of* $J(x_e)$ *have negative real parts*. There are no generalizations for the notions of focus, node, etc., in this case.

Limit cycles (stable or unstable) are defined here in the same way as in Section 1.2. However a variety of other interesting trajectories exist here. One is the case of *quasiperiodic* or *almost periodic* motions.

A quasiperiodic function $F(t)$ is one which can be written as

$$F(t) = G(\omega_1 t, ..., \omega_m t)$$

where G is a continuous and periodic function with respect to each one of its arguments (with period 2π). For example,

$$\sin \omega_1 t + \sin \omega_2 t$$

is a quasiperiodic function. It will be periodic only if ω_1 and ω_2 have a rational ratio.

An almost periodic function $F(t)$ is one which can be approximated arbitrarily close by a sum of trigonometric functions.

The trajectories of these motions stay within a limited region of the state space, especially if the frequencies ω_1, ω_2,..., ω_m are close to each other. In general such a region has a toroidal shape. An illustration of this can be obtained by considering a projection of a motion

$$x = a \sin \omega_1 t + b \sin \omega_2 t$$

on the $(x, dx/dt)$ plane.

Figure 1.4.1 shows a plot of the case of $\omega_2 = \frac{3}{4}\omega_1$ and $a = b = 1$.

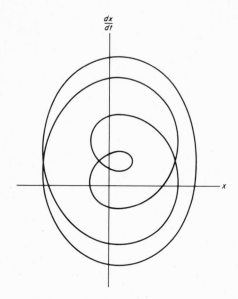

FIG. 1.4.1. Trajectories of a periodic system which can also be considered as quasi-periodic at a higher frequency.

This particular trajectory would be a limit cycle with period 2π. In this case, however, one could also speak about a *limit annulus* of "average" period $4\pi/7$. Macroscopically the behavior of the system could be approximated by a limit cycle of that period.

We will return to the study of such phenomena in Chapter 7 in connection with systems of populations of oscillators.

If Eq. (1.4.1) is linear and autonomous of the form

$$dx/dt = \mathbf{A}x \tag{1.4.4}$$

for some constant matrix $\mathbf{A}$, then the exact solution of the system will be

$$\mathbf{x}(t) = e^{\mathbf{A}t}\,\mathbf{x}(0) \tag{1.4.5}$$

If the eigenvalues of $\mathbf{A}$ are λ_1, λ_2,..., λ_n (distinct) and its eigenvectors $\mathbf{y}_1$, $\mathbf{y}_2$,..., $\mathbf{y}_n$, then the above solution can be expressed as

$$\mathbf{x}(t) = \sum_{i=1}^{n} a_i \mathbf{y}_i \, e^{\lambda_i t} \tag{1.4.6}$$

where a_i,..., a_n depend on the initial conditions.

We conclude the discussion of general nth-order dynamical systems by stating the well-known *Liapunov criterion* for their stability.

The autonomous system S described by

$$d\mathbf{x}/dt = \mathbf{f}(\mathbf{x})$$

has an asymptotically stable equilibrium point $\mathbf{x}_e$ with region of attraction the invariant set R if there exists a function $V(\mathbf{x})$ such that

(1) it has continuous partial derivatives $\partial V/\partial x_i$;
(2) it is positive for all $\mathbf{x} \in R$ except for $\mathbf{x}_e$ where it takes the value zero;
(3) its time derivative dV/dt along the trajectories of S, namely

$$\sum_{i=1}^{n} f_i(\mathbf{x}) \frac{\partial V}{\partial x_i}$$

is negative for all $\mathbf{x} \in R$ except for $\mathbf{x}_e$ where it takes the value zero.

If the last condition is relaxed to require that dV/dt is simply non-positive in R, then $\mathbf{x}_e$ will be neutrally stable.

The major defect of this method is that it offers no hint whatsoever about how to find the function $V(\mathbf{x})$. It tends to be of greater value in theoretical studies rather than the check of the stability of specific systems.

The concept of the region of attraction is essential for nonlinear systems, since a point of equilibrium can be asymptotically stable, but for some initial conditions the trajectories stay away from it (see example of the previous section).

Bibliographical Note. There are many texts covering the state space in the case of linear systems [Oga-I, Oga-II, Zad-I]. The subject of almost periodic functions is covered in a number of monographs [Bes-I]. Moser has presented a thorough analysis of quasiperiodic motions [Mos-1]. There exist many texts emphasizing Liapunov's method [LaS-I, Zub-I] and it is also covered in most modern texts on automatic and feedback control [Oga-I, Oga-II].

1.5 Asymptotic Techniques

The labor involved in the graphoanalytical procedures and the difficulty of studying oscillations in nonlinear systems of higher than second order has led to the development of a different approach than the phase plane techniques. This is applicable to *weakly nonlinear* systems, namely those where the nonlinear term depends on a "small" parameter ε, and for $\varepsilon = 0$ the system is linear. In this section we will describe this method for second-order systems and in Section 7.3 we will discuss its application in the study of oscillations of high-order systems.

The following equation gives the general form of a weakly nonlinear second-order system which is likely to present sustained oscillations, i.e., a limit cycle:

$$d^2x/dt^2 - \varepsilon f(x, dx/dt) + \omega^2 x = 0 \qquad (1.5.1)$$

When $\varepsilon = 0$ the system becomes an harmonic oscillator.

It seems reasonable to assume that when ε is not zero but sufficiently small then the solution for the approximating linear system should be close to the solution of the original system. Unfortunately this assumption is not justified in general. We will discuss this point in some detail later in Chapter 7. Here we note that for the case of systems of the form described by Eq. (1.5.1) it is justified only for the trajectory of the limit cycle (if one exists). Then the solution can be of the form

$$x = a \cos \psi + \varepsilon\, u_1(a, \psi) + \varepsilon^2\, u_2(a, \psi) + \cdots \qquad (1.5.2)$$

$$da/dt = \varepsilon A_1(a) + \varepsilon^2 A_2(a) + \cdots \qquad (1.5.3)$$

$$d\psi/dt = \omega + \varepsilon B_1(a) + \varepsilon^2 B_2(a) + \cdots \qquad (1.5.4)$$

For $\varepsilon = 0$ the solution becomes

$$x = a \cos \psi \qquad (1.5.5)$$

with a a constant and

$$\psi = \omega t + \psi_0 \qquad (1.5.6)$$

which is indeed the solution of the harmonic oscillator.

Notice that the convergence of the series appearing in Eqs. (1.5.2)–(1.5.4) can usually be guaranteed for sufficiently small ε. The difficult problem is to guarantee the convergence of truncated forms of these series to the true solution as ε tends to zero. Here we will assume that this is the case and we will be concerned only with determining the expressions $A_1(a)$ and $B_1(a)$; i.e., we will deal with a system consisting of Eq. (1.5.5) and

$$da/dt = \varepsilon A_1(a) \qquad (1.5.7)$$

$$d\psi/dt = \omega + \varepsilon B_1(a) \qquad (1.5.8)$$

This results in sufficiently good approximations in many practical problems.

We may now proceed to compute the derivatives of x from these equations while ignoring terms which are multiplied by powers of ε. We obtain

$$dx/dt = -a\omega \sin \psi + \varepsilon(A_1 \cos \psi - aB_1 \sin \psi) \qquad (1.5.9)$$

$$d^2x/dt^2 = -a\omega^2 \cos \psi - 2\omega\varepsilon(A_1 \sin \psi + aB_1 \cos \psi) \qquad (1.5.10)$$

These expressions [together with Eq. (1.5.5)] must now be replaced in Eq. (1.5.1) and then solved with respect to $A_1(a)$ and $B_1(a)$. However the following observation is pertinent. Since dx/dt is the sum of two terms, $f(x, dx/dt)$ can be expanded in a Taylor series of the form

$$f(x, -a\omega \sin \psi + \varepsilon Q) = f(x, -a\omega \sin \psi) + \varepsilon f_{x'}(x, -a\omega \sin \psi)Q$$
$$+ \varepsilon^2 f_{x'x'}(x, -a\omega \sin \psi)Q^2 + \cdots \qquad (1.5.11)$$

where

$$Q = A_1 \cos \psi - aB_1 \sin \psi$$

and $f_{x'}$, $f_{x'x'}$ denote the first and second derivatives of f with respect to its second argument.

Since f is multiplied by ε in Eq. (1.5.1), all the terms except the first will appear with an ε^2 (or a higher power of ε) factor and thus can be ignored.

In this way Eq. (1.5.1) becomes

$$-\varepsilon f(a \cos \psi, -a\omega \sin \psi) - 2\omega\varepsilon(A_1 \sin \psi + aB_1 \cos \psi) = 0 \qquad (1.5.12)$$

The term ε can now be factored out and the equation multiplied by $\sin \psi$ and integrated from 0 to 2π. This yields

$$A_1(a) = -\frac{1}{2\pi\omega} \int_0^{2\pi} f(a \cos \psi, -a\omega \sin \psi) \sin \psi \, d\psi \qquad (1.5.13)$$

Similarly Eq. (1.5.12) can be multiplied by $\cos \psi$ and integrated from 0 to 2π. This yields

$$B_1(a) = -\frac{1}{2\pi\omega a} \int_0^{2\pi} f(a \cos \psi, -a\omega \sin \psi) \cos \psi \, d\psi \qquad (1.5.14)$$

Thus $A_1(a)$ and $B_1(a)$ are nothing more than the fundamental terms (times a multiplicative constant) of the Fourier series expansion of $f(a \cos \psi, -a\omega \sin \psi)$.

One can easily verify that if f is an even function of its first argument, i.e.,

$$f(x, dx/dt) = f(-x, dx/dt) \tag{1.5.15}$$

then

$$A_1(a) = -\frac{1}{\pi\omega} \int_0^\pi f(a \cos \psi, -a \sin \psi) \sin \psi \, d\psi \tag{1.5.16}$$

$$B_1(a) = 0 \tag{1.5.17}$$

and therefore

$$d\psi/dt = \omega \tag{1.5.18}$$

If f is an even function of its second argument, i.e.,

$$f(x, dx/dt) = f(x, -dx/dt) \tag{1.5.19}$$

then

$$A_1(a) = 0 \tag{1.5.20}$$

$$B_1(a) = -\frac{1}{\pi\omega a} \int_0^{2\pi} f(a \cos \psi, -a \sin \psi) \cos \psi \, d\psi \tag{1.5.21}$$

and therefore

$$da/dt = 0 \tag{1.5.22}$$

In the first case the oscillations are approximately *isoperiodic*; i.e., the frequency does not depend on a except through higher-order terms. A typical example is the van der Pol oscillator where

$$f(x, dx/dt) = (1 - x^2) \, dx/dt \tag{1.5.23}$$

Equation (1.5.16) then gives

$$A_1(a) = \frac{a\omega}{\pi\omega} \int_0^\pi (1 - a^2 \cos^2 \psi) \sin^2 \psi \, d\psi$$

or

$$A_1(a) = (a/2)(1 - a^2/4) \tag{1.5.24}$$

and

$$da/dt = (\varepsilon a/2)(1 - a^2/4) \tag{1.5.25}$$

For a less than 2 the RHS (right-hand side) is positive and thus a increases. For a greater than 2 the RHS is negative and thus a decreases. Therefore the value

$$a = 2$$

is a stable singularity of Eq. (1.5.25) and the system is expected to have a stable steady solution approximated within ε by the equation

$$x(t) = 2 \cos(\omega t + \psi_0) \tag{1.5.26}$$

A typical example of the second case is given by a weakly nonlinear *conservative* oscillator with

$$f(x, dx/dt) = p(x)$$

where p is some function of x. Then Eq. (1.5.21) gives

$$B_1(a) = -\frac{1}{\pi \omega a} \int_0^\pi p(a \cos \psi) \cos \psi \, d\psi \tag{1.5.27}$$

In this case the oscillations will not be isoperiodic unless $B_1(a)$ is zero. This can happen only if p is an even function of its argument. Then the oscillations will be approximately isoperiodic. We will return to this question in more detail in Section 1.7.

Bibliographical Note.   Asymptotic techniques in various forms have been proposed and used by many investigators and their descriptions can be found in most texts on nonlinear systems. The method, in a somewhat different form, was first proposed by van der Pol in 1927. However, its most general, precise, and systematic formulation is due to the Russian mathematicians N. M. Krylov and N. N. Bogoliubov, who published their work first in 1937. The book by Bogoliubov and Mitropolsky [Bog-I] is still the best reference for the reader who wants to gain a deep understanding of asymptotic techniques. Many other texts [Bel-I, Fes-I, Mal-I, Min-I, Mit-I] offer treatments of this and related methods. However, most standard control theory textbooks do not cover it.

1.6   Describing Function

A technique with some similarities to the ones described in the previous section, but also with essential differences, involves the use of the *describing function*. It is applicable to systems where the nonlinearity is isolated from the rest of the dynamics. The following is the general form of such a system:

$$S: \begin{cases} d\mathbf{x}/dt = \mathbf{A}\mathbf{x} + \mathbf{b}u & (1.6.1) \\[2mm] \sigma = \sum_{i=1}^{n} c_i x_i & (1.6.2) \\[2mm] u = f(\sigma) & (1.6.3) \end{cases}$$

where $\mathbf{x}$ and $\mathbf{b}$ are n-dimensional vectors and $\mathbf{A}$ an $n \times n$ matrix. In spite of the limited form of S, its study is of interest because other types of nonlinear systems can be approximated by it.

Suppose that a monofrequency oscillation is present in the system. Then

$$\mathbf{x}(t) = \mathbf{a}\, e^{j\omega t} \tag{1.6.4}$$

where $\mathbf{a}$ is a complex vector. (This is necessary in order to allow different phases among the components of $\mathbf{x}$.) Substituting this expression into Eqs. (1.6.1) and (1.6.2) we obtain

$$j\omega \mathbf{a}\, e^{j\omega t} = \mathbf{A}\mathbf{a}\, e^{j\omega t} + \mathbf{b}u \tag{1.6.5}$$

$$\sigma = \left(\sum_{i=1}^{n} c_i a_i \right) e^{j\omega t} \tag{1.6.6}$$

Then $f(\sigma)$ will also have an oscillation of frequency ω but with a nonsinusoidal waveform. We may proceed with its Fourier series expansion which, if we define

$$c = \left(\sum_{i=1}^{n} c_i a_i \right) \tag{1.6.7}$$

will be of the form

$$f(c\, e^{j\omega t}) = \sum_{k=0}^{\infty} f_k(c)\, e^{j\omega k t} \tag{1.6.8}$$

where $f_k(c)$ are complex amplitudes.

Substituting this into Eq. (1.6.1) we obtain

$$\frac{d\mathbf{x}}{dt} = \mathbf{A}\mathbf{x} + \mathbf{b}\, f_0(c) + \mathbf{b}\, f_1(c)\, e^{j\omega t} + \mathbf{b} \sum_{k=2}^{\infty} f_k(c)\, e^{j\omega k t} \tag{1.6.9}$$

Under certain conditions the solution of this linear equation may attenuate high-frequency terms; i.e., it may act as a low pass filter. If this is indeed the case, then the sum in the RHS of Eq. (1.6.9) can be ignored. Thus we approximate in effect the output of a nonlinearity by its *first harmonic term*. Note that for many types of nonlinearities the higher harmonics have smaller amplitude to start with. Thus if the output is a square wave, the kth harmonic has amplitude only $1/k$ times the amplitude of the fundamental. This fact in addition to the common occurrence of practical systems where the linear part acts as a low pass filter renders the describing function a widely useful concept.

If the sum in the RHS of Eq. (1.6.9) is ignored, then the latter may be combined with Eq. (1.6.5) into

$$j\omega\mathbf{a}\,e^{j\omega t} = [\mathbf{A}\mathbf{a} + \mathbf{b}\,f_1(c)]\,e^{j\omega t} + \mathbf{b}f_0(c) \qquad (1.6.10)$$

A necessary condition for the validity of this equation is that $f_0(c) = 0$. This will be true if and only if f is an antisymmetric nonlinearity, namely that

$$f(\sigma) = -f(-\sigma) \qquad (1.6.11)$$

Then Eq. (1.6.10) is equivalent to

$$\mathbf{A}\mathbf{a} + \mathbf{b}f_1(c) - \mathbf{a}j\omega = 0 \qquad (1.6.12)$$

If this is true, then solution (1.6.4) is indeed possible. In other words, Eq. (1.6.12) gives a condition for the existence of oscillations with frequency ω in the system. This breaks into $2n$ real scalar equations with $2n + 1$ unknowns: ω and the real and imaginary parts for a_1, a_2,..., a_n. An additional condition is obtained by the requirement that $\mathbf{x}(t)$ is a real vector. This can be seen best by writing Eq. (1.6.4) as

$$x_1(t) = a_1 \sin \omega t$$
$$x_2(t) = a_2 \sin(\omega t + \phi_2)$$
$$\vdots$$
$$x_n(t) = a_n \sin(\omega t + \phi_n)$$

Since the origin of time is immaterial, ϕ_1 can be set arbitrarily equal to zero; thus, there are only $2n$ unknowns.

The usual way of expressing condition (1.6.12) is through the use of the concept of transfer function. Indeed multiplying Eq. (1.6.12) by the inverse of the matrix $(\mathbf{A} - j\omega\mathbf{I})$ yields

$$(\mathbf{A} - j\omega\mathbf{I})^{-1}\mathbf{b}\,f_1(c) + \mathbf{a} = 0$$

Let now $\mathbf{c} = (c_1, c_2,..., c_n)$. Then taking the scalar product of this equation with $\mathbf{c}$ and noticing that $c = \mathbf{c}'\mathbf{a}$, we obtain

$$\mathbf{c}'(\mathbf{A} - j\omega\mathbf{I})^{-1}\mathbf{b}\,f_1(c) + c = 0 \qquad (1.6.13)$$

The expression $-\mathbf{c}'(\mathbf{A} - j\omega\mathbf{I})^{-1}\mathbf{b}$ is called the *transfer function* $G(j\omega)$ of the linear part of the system. The justification for this name becomes obvious if we notice that when

$$u = u_0\, e^{j\omega t}$$

then

$$\sigma = G(j\omega)\, u_0\, e^{j\omega t}$$

Equation (1.6.13) then becomes

$$-G(j\omega)f_1(c) + c = 0$$

Finally we define as the *describing function of the nonlinearity* the complex ratio of the first harmonic of the output over the input, namely

$$D(c) = f_1(c)/c \qquad (1.6.14)$$

and the final condition for oscillations of frequency ω with amplitude of σ equal to c becomes:

$$G(j\omega)\, D(c) = 1 \qquad (1.6.15)$$

This equation can be solved graphically by finding the intersection of the two curves defined by $G(j\omega)$ and $1/D(c)$ in the complex plane. Indeed, consider the following example:

$$\dot{x}_1 = -u, \qquad \dot{x}_2 = -ax_2 + x_1\,, \qquad \dot{x}_3 = -bx_3 + x_2$$

$$u = 1 \quad \text{if} \quad x_3 > 0, \qquad u = -1 \quad \text{if} \quad x_3 < 0$$

It can be readily verified that the transfer function of the system is

$$G(j\omega) = -1/j\omega(j\omega + a)(j\omega + b) \qquad (1.6.16)$$

and the output of the nonlinearity for a sinewave input is a square wave of amplitude one. The amplitude of its first harmonic is $4/\pi$ and therefore

$$D(c) = 4/\pi c \qquad (1.6.17)$$

Figure 1.6.1 shows the plots of $-G(j\omega)$ and $-1/D(c)$.*
If $b = a$, then it can be easily verified that the intersection occurs for

$$\omega = a \qquad \text{and} \qquad c = 2/\pi a^3$$

---

* These functions were used in order to make the plot similar to the ones found in the engineering literature [Gel-I, Gib-I, Oga-II].

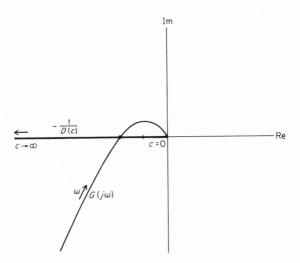

FIG. 1.6.1. Plots in the complex plane of the transfer function and the negative inverse of the describing function. Their intersection determines the amplitude and frequency of oscillations.

Thus the sustained oscillations have the same frequency as the characteristic frequency of the system and their amplitude is a decreasing function of that frequency. The latter observation is valid for a large class of systems.

If Eq. (1.6.15) has no solution, then no oscillations are possible, unless the system deviates significantly from the assumptions under which this method is applicable.

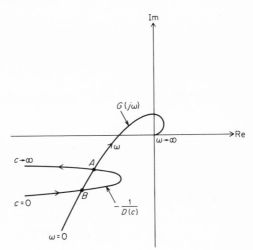

FIG. 1.6.2. Testing the stability of oscillations on the basis of the plots of the transfer function and the negative inverse of the describing function.

Note that finding pairs of (c, ω) satisfying Eq. (1.6.15) does not mean that such oscillations will be observed. We must also verify that the resulting periodic solution is stable. A rigorous answer to this question is not easy. The following is a useful rule of thumb.

If the plot of $G(j\omega)$ intersects the plot of $-1/D(c)$ so that the increase

TABLE 1.6.1

Describing Functions for Various Nonlinearities

Nonlinear function $f(x)$	Real part of $D(c)$	Imaginary part of $D(c)$
1 x^3	$\frac{3}{4}c^2$	0
2 (step function graph, level M and $-M$)	$\dfrac{4M}{\pi c}$	0
3 (saturation graph, slope to level a, breakpoints $-a$, a)	1 $\dfrac{2}{\pi}\left\{\sin^{-1}\dfrac{a}{c}+\dfrac{a}{c}\left[1-\left(\dfrac{a}{c}\right)^2\right]^{1/2}\right\}$	0 if $\dfrac{c}{a}\leqslant 1$ 0 if $\dfrac{c}{a}>1$
4 (deadzone graph, breakpoints $-a$, a)	0 $1-\dfrac{2}{\pi}\left\{\sin^{-1}\dfrac{a}{c}+\dfrac{a}{c}\left[1-\left(\dfrac{a}{c}\right)^2\right]^{1/2}\right\}$	0 if $\dfrac{c}{a}\leqslant 1$ 0 if $\dfrac{c}{a}>1$
5 (hysteresis relay graph, level M, width d)	0 $\dfrac{4M}{\pi c}\left[1-\left(\dfrac{d}{c}\right)^2\right]^{1/2}$	0 if $\dfrac{c}{d}\leqslant 1$ $-\dfrac{4Md}{\pi c^2}$ if $\dfrac{c}{d}>1$

in c moves from right to left (as in Fig. 1.6.1), then the oscillations are stable; otherwise they are unstable.

For example, in Fig. 1.6.2 point A corresponds to stable oscillations and point B to unstable ones. A discussion of this rule can be found in the text by Ogata [Oga-II], while a detailed analysis of the question of stability has been presented by Geld and Vander Velde [Gel-I].

Table 1.6.1 gives a list of the describing functions of certain common nonlinearities. One can see that if the *nonlinearity is single valued* then the describing function is *real*. This is indeed a true generalization, and a formal proof for it can be found in most texts.

Bibliographic Note. The method of describing function has been used widely by control engineers and there is a substantial periodical literature about it as well as a number of thorough treatments in textbooks [Gel-I, Gib-I, Oga-II, etc.). In the latter the reader can find more examples and extensive tables of describing functions for various nonlinearities.

1.7 Conservative Systems

These form a special class of nonlinear systems which have attracted the interest of researchers for a number of reasons, not the least important being that one can analyze their behavior in more depth than other systems. For simplicity we will study here only the case of an oscillator with one degree of freedom described by the equation

$$d^2x/dt^2 + g(x) = 0 \qquad (1.7.1)$$

where $g(x)$ is a continuous function such that $g(0) = 0$. Multiplying both sides of the equation by dx/dt and integrating we obtain

$$\left(\frac{dx}{dt}\right)^2 + 2\int_0^x g(u)\, du = \text{const} \equiv c \qquad (1.7.2)$$

If it is true that

$$xg(x) > 0 \qquad \text{for} \quad x \neq 0 \qquad (1.7.3)$$

in some interval $(a, b)(ab < 0)$, then it can be shown that Eq. (1.7.2) represents *closed trajectories* centered at the origin $(0, 0)$, which is a *center* for this system. For any initial conditions within a region R, the motion will be periodic with amplitude depending only on these initial conditions.

The harmonic oscillator

$$d^2x/dt^2 + \omega^2 x = 0 \qquad (1.7.4)$$

represents the simplest special case of such a system. Its trajectories are concentric circles if the scale $1/\omega_0$ is used for the x axis. The frequency of oscillations is always ω_0.

The name conservative is given to such systems because they "conserve" the value of the left-hand side of Eq. (1.7.2). For many physical systems this corresponds to energy.

In general, the period T of oscillators will be different along each trajectory. If a and b are the two values of x for which $dx/dt = 0$ (Fig. 1.7.1), then it is easily seen from Eq. (1.7.2) that

$$T = 2 \int_a^b \frac{dx}{(c - 2 \int_0^x g(u)\,du)^{1/2}} \qquad (1.7.5)$$

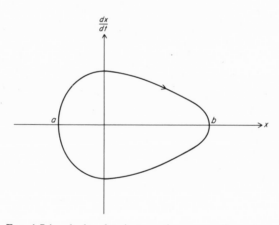

Fig. 1.7.1.   A closed trajectory of a conservative system.

For example, consider the case when

$$g(x) = x^3 \qquad (1.7.6)$$

Then Eq. (1.7.2) becomes

$$(dx/dt)^2 + x^4/2 = c \qquad (1.7.7)$$

and

$$a = -(2c)^{1/4}, \qquad b = (2c)^{1/4}$$

while

$$T = 2 \int_{-(2c)^{1/4}}^{(2c)^{1/4}} \frac{dx}{(c - x^4/2)^{1/2}} \tag{1.7.8}$$

A change of variables

$$u = x/(2c)^{1/4}$$

yields the following:

$$T = 2(2/c)^{1/4} \int_{-1}^{1} \frac{du}{(1 - u^4)^{1/2}} \tag{1.7.9}$$

The integral is independent of c and therefore the period is inversely proportional to the fourth root of c.

Urabe [Ura-I] has considered the case of *isoperiodism* or *isochronism*, when T is independent of c. He has shown that if $g(x)$ is also differentiable at $x = 0$ then a necessary and sufficient condition for isoperiodism is that $g(x)$ be of such form that for some arbitrary continuous odd function $S(x)$ one has

$$g \left\{ \frac{\omega_0}{2\pi} \int_0^x [1 + S(u)] \, du \right\} = \frac{2\pi}{\omega_0} \frac{x}{1 + S(x)} \tag{1.7.10}$$

This can be readily verified for a linear system by taking $S(x) = 0$, which results in $g(x) = x$.

Besides linear, one can also find nonlinear systems which are isoperiodic. For example, for $S(x) = x$, $\omega_0 = 2\pi$ and

$$g(x) = 1 - 1/(1 + 2x)^{1/2} \tag{1.7.11}$$

Equation (1.7.10) is satisfied as well as Eq. (1.7.3) and the other conditions, provided that

$$x > -\tfrac{1}{2}$$

Figure 1.7.2 shows a family for close trajectories whose equations are

$$(dx/dt)^2 + 2x - 2(1 + 2x)^{1/2} = c \tag{1.7.12}$$

c varies between -2 and -1. The first value corresponds to the center while the last one to the outermost closed trajectory. A straightforward but lengthy application of Eq. (1.7.5) shows that the period is equal to 2π.

It should be pointed out that the property of isoperiodism depends on the precise choice of the form of $g(x)$. For example, if

$$g(x) = 0.9 - 1/(1 + 2x)^{1/2}$$

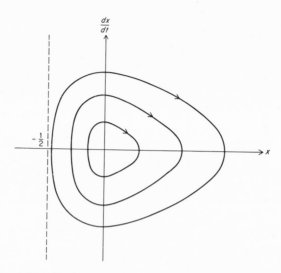

FIG. 1.7.2.   Trajectories of an isoperiodic conservative system.

the resulting system does not have that property. On the other hand, a linear system contains only one parameter, ω_0 [since $g(x) = x$], and any changes in its value will not affect the property of isoperiodism. Therefore *linear* are the only *conservative* systems which have periods independent of both the initial conditions and the *exact* value of parameters (see also Section 7.2, Theorem 7.22).

On the other hand, nonconservative systems with limit cycles are in effect "isochrone" in the sense that for all initial conditions the system oscillates with the period of the limit cycle. Furthermore in Section 1.5 we have seen systems which are isoperiodic throughout the phase plane.

Bibliographical Note.   Most texts on nonlinear systems [And-I, Min-I] contain sections on conservative systems. Urabe's book [Ura-I] presents an advanced treatment.

CHAPTER 2

Examples of Biological Rhythms

2.1 Introduction

We will list in this chapter a series of examples of biological oscillators. Although the existence of biological rhythms was well known since antiquity, the existence of biological oscillators has been accepted only recently. A prominent view (which is still held by a number of researchers) was that the rhythms were due to external periodic effects like the daily changes of light and dark or similar changes in temperature, etc. This view was expressed more often about oscillations with a long period since high-frequency oscillations like these involved in the heartbeat were of a more obviously endogenous nature. It will take us too far off our track if we give a detailed historical account about the objections raised to the existence of endogenous biological oscillators. Today the evidence in favor of "biological clocks" is overwhelming, as we will see in the various sections of this chapter.

Our emphasis throughout this monograph will be on oscillations with long periods, usually of the order of 24 hours. They have received considerable attention, especially for the last twenty years, for many reasons. It is obvious that they are of major importance in many biological functions: for example, susceptibility to drugs shows a daily rhythm. Also airplane travel across time zones (as well as space travel) has brought up the problems of adjusting the rhythms of a subject to cycles of a different phase. A second reason is their universality. With the exception of bacteria and simpler organisms, all other living forms which have been checked show such rhythms. Third, the biological mechanism responsible for the rhythms remains a mystery. Not only that, but it seems to be insensitive to most chemical agents. Finally, the long time scale involved allows the performance of experiments which study in detail various dynamical properties of the rhythms. High-frequency oscillations (e.g., of the electrical activity in cardiac muscle tissue) are not as easily subject to detailed manipulation.

We cover briefly additional types of oscillators and, in particular, those involving enzymatic reactions.

2.2 Circadian Rhythms

The work of many researchers, especially during this century, has resulted in an impressive accumulation of experimental evidence which strongly suggests the existence of endogenous oscillators in living systems. In particular it seems that daily cycles of biological phenomena are controlled by such oscillators rather than by the alternation of light and darkness in their environment.

One argument in favor of this theory is that organisms kept in carefully controlled environments, where the temperature and light intensity were kept constant, still exhibit a periodicity in their behavior. The period of such rhythms is almost always different than 24 hours—in general, varying between 22 and 26 hours. Usually, but not always, for a given individual organism the value of the period remains unchanged with the passage of time. Figure 2.2.1 shows a typical way of plotting experimental data of this kind. Each line represents 24 hours,

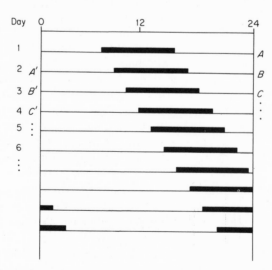

Fig. 2.2.1. A typical way of presenting data illustrating periodic activity of an organism.

with the data for each day plotted in succession. The heavy lines represent intervals of "active" behavior and the thin lines intervals of "inactive" behavior. It can be seen that the "active" phase starts (and ends) every 26 hours. (Note that points A and A' are actually representing the same time instance; also B and B', C and C', etc.)

Figure 2.2.2 shows a photograph of an actual record of the locomotor

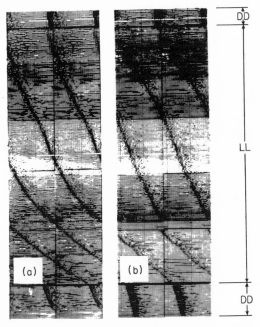

FIG. 2.2.2. Record of locomotor activity of a hamster [Pit-9]. LL denotes a period of constant illumination and DD a period of darkness.

activity of a hamster. The start of the activity has a period of a little over 24 hours.

Because the period of the rhythms is rarely, if ever, exactly 24 hours, Halberg suggested the term *circadian* (from the Latin "circa diem"; i.e., about a day) for such phenomena.

It is beyond the scope of this monograph to give a complete survey of the many very interesting experiments which have been performed in this field. Bünning's book can serve as an introduction to the experimental literature [Bün-A]. A series of volumes containing the proceedings of symposia on rhythms held about every five years is helpful for acquainting a newcomer to the field with the main experimental results [Col-A, Asc-A, Men-A]. A number of additional survey books [Bro-A,

Har-A, Luc-A (extensive bibliography), Sol-A, Swe-A, Wit-A, etc.] and papers [Asc-1, Asc-2, Asc-4, Asc-11, Asc-12, Halb-1, Halb-2, Has-2, Hil-1, Hof-9, McC-1, Men-3, Pit-3, Pit-4, Swe-2, Van-1] are available. Examples of the wide variety of functions which seem to exhibit a circadian rhythm can be found throughout the literature [Asc-6, Asc-8, von B-1, Hau-1, Kol-1, Mur-1, Pan-1, Str-1, etc.]. The following are two major observations about the dynamics of such rhythms.

(1) Entrainment by Temperature and Light Cycles. The behavior of the organism can be made to follow periodic changes of light intensity and/or temperature of its environment. This followup is commonly referred to as entrainment or synchronization. It is possible only if the period of the external cycle is close to the endogenous period or to integer multiples or submultiples of it. Figure 2.2.3 shows this phenomenon for the locomotor activity of a cockroach. The animal originally *free runs* in constant dark and at the twelfth day a photo-

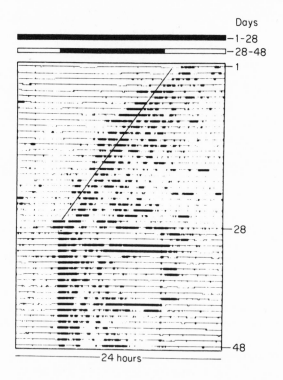

Fɪɢ. 2.2.3. Entrainment of the locomotor activity of a cockroach [Rob-2].

periodic regime is applied. We will discuss in detail the analytical and biological aspects of entrainment in Chapter 4.

(2) Phase Shifts Caused by Nonrepetitive Stimuli. Figure 2.2.4 shows a change in the phase of the locomotor rhythm of a flying squirrel

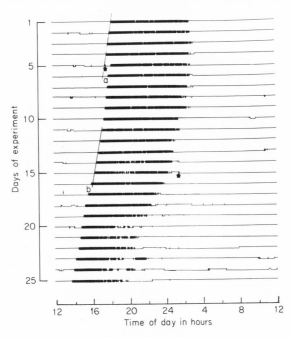

FIG. 2.2.4. Phase shifting of the locomotor activity of a flying squirrel by a brief light pulse. A pulse at *a* causes an advance, while at *b* it causes a delay [DeC-2].

by its exposure to a brief increase in light intensity (0.5 ft-c for 10 min). The amount of the phase shift depends on both the features of the stimulus itself and its timing with respect to the endogenous rhythm. The latter relationship is of great importance in the study of biological oscillators and it will be discussed extensively in Chapter 3. It should be emphasized that such perturbations can be caused by both light and temperature changes as well as by chemical agents.

In retrospect, neither one of these properties is surprising for a "clock" whose function is the control of the behavior of the organism with respect to its environment. They point out also the major advantage of the possession of such a regulator by a living system.

If the behavior of an organism was directly controlled by its environment it would necessarily involve time lags between the occurrence, say, of daylight and the change in behavior. Furthermore, it would be quite sensitive to perturbations of more or less random nature. Indeed consider the example of an individual sleeping in a room without curtains who expects to be awakened by daylight. Not only must he "lose" a number of hours after sunrise but also he may sleep through a cloudy day.

On the other hand, the possession of an inner clock synchronized to the external environment allows an organism to respond faster and in a more reliable way to the daily environmental changes. For example, most humans set their waking-up hour either by habit (i.e., an inner clock!) or by an alarm clock rather than by sunlight. In other words, an inner clock allows the establishment of *predictive control* whose advantages are well known to control engineers. For an additional discussion of this point the reader is referred to the literature [Bün-4, Pit-4].

The ability to predict the occurrence of certain events offers an obvious advantage for survival, and it is not surprising that such a "clock" seems to exist in almost any organism which has been studied, from humans and other mammals down to insects, plants, and even unicellular organisms [Men-A]. We will use the term *circadian clock* to describe this controller. The singular form used for the word "clock" does not presume any constraints on the structure of the system. As we shall see later (Chapters 7 and 8), there is strong evidence that the controller consists of a group of mutually coupled oscillators. Under normal conditions these units are synchronized and behave as a single oscillator. On the other hand, there exists evidence that a given organism may contain more than one *independent* clock, each controlling a different function. This seems to be particularly true in humans and higher animals [Asc-7, Asc-10] while the opposite holds for unicellular organisms [McM-1]. There a single system controls a number of different functions. In the rest of this book the term circadian clock will be used with the understanding that it refers to an independent controller (subject, of course, to environmental influences) of a specific type of overt behavior. It should also be pointed out that the circadian clock is genetically determined [Bru-5, Fel-3, Kon-1, Pit-8, Ric-1].

2.3   Circadian Rhythms in an Insect Population

A rhythm which has been studied extensively is the eclosion of the fruitfly *Drosophila pseudoobscura* [Pit-7, Pit-8, Pit-10, Win-3, Zim-1,

Chan-1]. Under natural conditions insects emerge from pupae just before dawn when the humidity of the environment is usually highest. The importance of a "clock" for such an organism need not be over-emphasized. Since the transition is a "one-shot" phenomenon, the rhythm can be observed only in a population of pupae of different ages. It is possible to record the number of flies emerging every hour and thus form a histogram of this number for various of the day. Figure 2.3.1a

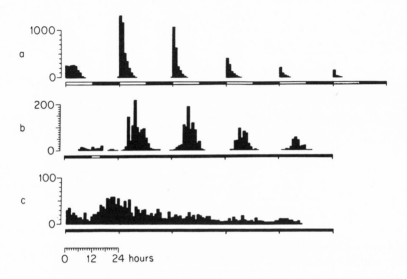

Fig. 2.3.1.   Eclosion peaks in a pupalation of fruitfly pupae [Pit-4].

shows such a plot obtained from a population exposed to alternating light and dark cycles of 12 hours each. Figure 2.3.1b shows a similar plot obtained under constant darkness after a single exposure to light. The time medians of the histograms peaks are used to assay the rhythm.

When the organism is exposed to even dim continuous light a damping of the rhythm is observed. Eclosion continues but it is arrhythmic [Fig. 2.3.1c]. The obvious explanation for this is that eclosion is caused by a maturation process while the "clock" opens a "gate" at certain times of the day which facilitates that process. If the gate remains closed (or continuously open), then arrhythmic eclosion will result.

Light pulses of very short duration (a few minutes) can cause substantial phase shifts of the rhythm, and this makes it a desirable object for study of the dynamics of biological oscillations. Furthermore, although macroscopically one observes a series of transients before the new phase is achieved, there is evidence that the change in the state of the regulator occurs within a very short time.

Because of the wealth of systematic experimental data about this rhythm, it has been central in the development of various models and it will be often used as an example in the sequence. However, there are certain disadvantages associated with the use of such a rhythm as a prime subject for the study of the dynamics of circadian oscillators. The "one-shot" nature of the observed phenomenon limits the number of cycles which can be observed in a given culture. The time required for the development of pupae is about 9 days and, even if one starts with the widest possible age distribution, it cannot be observed for more than 8 or 9 cycles. Therefore only "short duration" experiments can be attempted. Another disadvantage (at least for certain studies) is the lack of a graduated response to light intensity.

2.4   Circadian Rhythms in Cell Populations

Unicellular organisms and in particular various algae present many rhythms which are relatively easy to observe.

(1)   Growth and Division Rhythms.   In general a population of cells that is growing by division can be assumed to satisfy an equation of the following form:

$$dN = R(t)\,N(t)\,dt \tag{2.4.1}$$

where dN represents the change in the number of cells $N(t)$ between time t and $t + dt$ and $R(t)$ represents the rate of cell division. If it is constant, say R_0, then a straightforward integration of this equation shows that the population will exhibit an exponential growth:

$$N(t) = N(0)\exp[R_0 t] \tag{2.4.2}$$

The generation time T_g during which the population doubles its size will be given by

$$T_g = (1/R_0)\ln 2 \tag{2.4.3}$$

Such cell cultures are usually called logarithmic.

Under certain conditions it is possible to obtain *synchronous* cultures which are characterized by the fact that $R(t) = 0$ for most of the time as shown in Fig. 2.4.1. Then, between t_1 and t_2, $N(t)$ remains constant while between t_2 and t_3 it undergoes a steep change. If the time $t_3 - t_1$ is greater or equal to the time T_g, then

$$N(t_3)/N(t_1) = 2 \tag{2.4.4}$$

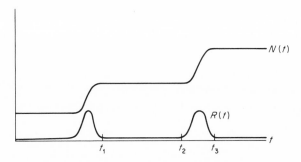

Fig. 2.4.1. Synchronous growth of all cell population. The ordinate corresponds to number of cells N for the top curve and the rate of division R for the bottom curve.

If the peaks in $R(t)$ are equally spaced but less than T_g, then subsequent size steps will be negatively correlated. This has been observed in cultures of *Euglena gracilis* [Edm-4].

The rhythmicity can be induced either by temperature or by light cycles or by single pulses. The rhythm continues to persist under constant light and temperature conditions and it can be entrained within wide limits by various photoperiodic regimes. Generally the system behaves as though a self-sustained nonlinear oscillator gates cell division. Examples of such experiments as well as other rhythms in cell populations have been described by many researchers [von M-A, Zeu-A, Bru-3, Bru-4, Edm-1, Edm-2, Edm-3, Edm-4, Edm-5, Edm-6, Has-1, Will-1, Will-2, etc.].

(2) **Phototactic Rhythms.** Many algae respond to light by swimming toward its source. This offers a convenient way of experimental measurements: namely, a light beam is directed through a culture and the degree by which it is obscured is a measure of the phototactic response. Figure 2.4.2 shows a typical record of the time course of obscuring the light by successive light pulses. The envelop of the maxima shows a clear rhythm. A number of circadian phototactic rhythms are described in the literature [Bri-1, Bri-2, Bru-4, Has-1, Will-3, etc.].

(3) **Biochemical Rhythms.** One can measure the rate at which various reactions proceed at various times of the day. In a number of instances such rates present a circadian periodicity. Feldman reports that for the rate of amino acid incorporation in *Euglena gracilis* [Fel-2], and Fogel and Hastings describe the same phenomenon for the photosynthetic capacity of *Gonyaulax polyedra* [Fog-1]. We will return to

Fig. 2.4.2. Outline of a record of phototactic rhythm of a population of algae. When the culture is exposed to light the algae swim towards it, thus obscuring it. The abscissa is time while the ordinate denotes the degree of motion as measured by the drop in light intensity received by a photocell. Higher values of the ordinate correspond to lower values of light intensity. (See Bruce and Pittendrigh [Bru-1] or Bruce [Bru-2] for details.)

this subject in the next section where we will describe biochemical oscillators with periods much shorter than 24 hours.

(4) Luminescence Related Rhythms. Many species of algae present circadian rhythms associated with various aspects of their luminance [Has-1].

It has been recently shown that at least in one species its rhythms behave as though a single master clock controls a number of them and, in particular, cell division, photosynthetic capacity, glow, and luminescence capacity [McM-1]. This is not true for other circadian rhythms. For example, humans can exhibit "daily" cycles of rest and activity at a different period than their temperature cycle [Asc-10].

The study of circadian (or other) rhythms in microorganisms is more likely to help us understand the nature of the clock than studies in higher-order organisms. Indeed the simpler the organism the lesser the probability that the output of the circadian regulator will not be obscured by intermediate systems as much as it would in a higher-order organism. Also it is easier to study the effect of chemical agents on the clock. In a higher organism such agents may never reach the basic regulator because of the complex metabolic systems involved.

2.5 Biochemical Oscillators

The study of chemical kinetics reveals that it is indeed possible to have sustained oscillations of the concentration of a chemical substance. Such an oscillator could serve as the clock described in the previous section. Prigogine and his co-workers have studied this problem extensively within the framework of thermodynamics and have described systems which can show oscillations not only in time but also in space [Pri-1, Pri-2, Pri-3, Pri-4, Pri-5, Pri-6, Lav-1, Lef-1, Lef-2, Lef-3, Ede-1]. Chance, Pye, Packer, and their co-workers as well as other investigators have provided experimental evidence of such oscillations at the cellular level [Bet-1, Bet-2, Cha-1, Cha-2, Cha-3, Dea-1, Fre-1, van G-2, Hes-1, Pac-1, Pye-1, Pye-2, Pye-3, Pye-4, Uts-1], and Zhabotinsky and others have studied oscillations in inorganic media [Bus-1, Frü-1, Zai-1, Zha-1, Zha-2]. Selkov, Higgins, and others have described various forms of enzyme catalyzed reactions which can show oscillations [Fra-A, Hig-1, Hig-2, Sel-1, Sel-2, Sel-3, Sel-4, Sel-5, Bel-1, Com-1, See-1, See-2, See-3, Wal-1]. A collection of papers on these subjects can be found in [Cha-A].

Chance and Pye have studied, in particular, oscillations of DPNH (diphosphopyridine nucleotide) in yeast cells. This substance has a number of properties which make feasible highly accurate and fast measurements of its concentration in both intact cells and in extracts [Cha-2, Cha-3]. Figure 2.5.1 shows a train of oscillations of DPNH

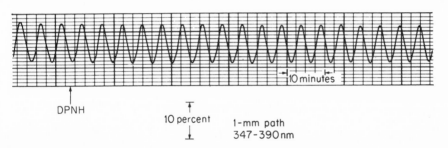

FIG. 2.5.1. Waveform of DPNH oscillations [Cha-3].

in cell-free extract of the yeast *Saccharomyces carlsbergensis*. DPNH participates in the metabolism of glucose in such organisms.

The waveform of the oscillations can take a wide variety of forms, as shown in Figs. 2.5.2 and 2.5.3. Additional examples can be found in the scientific literature quoted above. These forms can be observed only in cell-free extracts, while only sinusoidal waveforms are observed in intact cells [Pye-3]. However, this need not indicate any fundamental difference in the mechanism of oscillations in the two cases. The manipulation of the waveform is achieved by the addition of various substances to extracts (e.g., Apyrase [Pye-3]). The intact cell membrane simply blocks out any such additions and therefore manipulation is not possible.

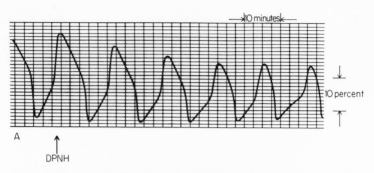

FIG. 2.5.2.   Waveform of DPNH oscillations [Cha-3].

Additions of chemicals and, in particular, ADP (adenosine-5-diphosphate) can cause substantial phase shifts of the oscillation instantaneously. Furthermore, the direction and value of the shift depends on the point of the cycle where the ADP addition was made [Pye-3]. (See also Fig. 3.3.7 in the next chapter.) Figure 2.5.4 shows the form of the change. Obviously the time derivative of the concentration of DPNH has a discontinuity at the point of ADP addition. In terms of the dynamical systems discussed in the previous chapter this implies that the right-hand side of one of Eqs. (1.2.1)–(1.2.2) or Eqs. (1.4.1) undergoes a discontinuous (or very fast) change. This means either that the concentration of ADP appears explicitly in these expressions or that one of the variables present has a concentration which can be modified by ADP at a speed much higher than that of the other reactions involved in the oscillation. In such a case the dynamics of the reaction between ADP and substance X can be ignored, and then the concentration of X can be expressed as a simple function of that of ADP. Thus its concentration will appear again explicitly in the state equations. If it remained invariant with time, then one would expect to see a difference in the waveform and/or frequency of the oscillations after the addition. That this does not happen means that ADP (or X) is "consumed" during the reaction, or, in the terminology of Section 1.4,

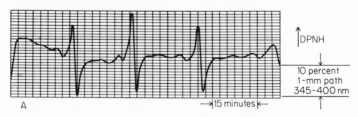

FIG. 2.5.3.   Waveform of DPNH oscillations [Cha-3].

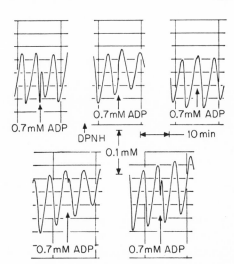

FIG. 2.5.4. Phase shifting of an
DPNH oscillation by the addition
of ADP [Pye-2].

it is a state variable. This conclusion is hardly surprising in view of our
knowledge about the dynamics of the glycolytic chain. Nevertheless it
illustrates the fact that any agent whose addition causes a sudden phase
shift of an oscillation without subsequent changes in waveform on
frequency must cause a discontinuous charge in a state variable or it
might be a state variable itself. In other words, it cannot be simply a
parameter of the dynamic equations of the system. We will discuss this
point in more detail in Section 6.2.

In spite of certain similarities between the oscillations in the glycolytic
chain and circadian rhythms there seems to be no connections between
the two. The time scales involved are of different orders of magnitude
and the effects of temperature on the two types are drastically different.
Nevertheless the study of the DPNH oscillations is worthwhile for
one interested in low-frequency rhythms. Their experimental accesibility
has allowed the building of quantitative models for biochemical
oscillations. It is not unreasonable to accept that the same type of
dynamics may govern the behavior of other biochemical oscillators and,
in particular, those involved in the circadian clock. This in turn would
allow the formulation of more concrete hypotheses about the nature
of the latter.

2.6 Neural Oscillators

There are numerous examples of periodically firing neurons in the
nervous system of various animals. A study of models of neural

membrane dynamics, as well as direct observations, shows that a neuron can keep firing at a constant rate for long periods of time. This may be considered as the simplest possible example of a neural oscillator. However, a more interesting case is presented by units which fire bursts of pulses periodically, as shown in Fig. 2.6.1a.

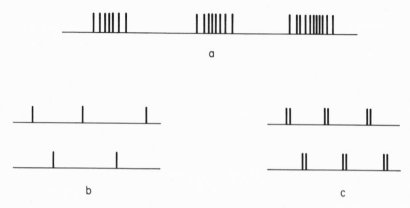

FIG. 2.6.1.   Patterns of periodic neuronal activity.

One can visualize a number of simple neural networks which would give rise to such a pattern. Before reviewing such models we should mention two important examples of such oscillatory behavior.

(a) **Control of the Flying System of Locusts.** It has been shown by Wilson [Wils-1, Wils-2, Wils-3, Wils-4, Pag-1] that the firing patterns on the neurons controlling the motion of the wings of this insect do not depend on proprioceptor feedback nor is there a direct correspondence between its pulses and the ones produced by the central nervous system. The latter seems to control only the overall frequency and level of oscillations and be responsible for switching from the pattern shown in Fig. 2.6.1b to the one of Fig. 2.6.1c and vice versa [Wils-1]. Wilson concluded that there was strong evidence in favor of a group of neural oscillators which generate the oscillatory patterns. The frequency of the oscillations is then controlled by external inputs to that group either from other parts of the central nervous systems or from various sensors.

(b) **Firing of Cells of Aplysia and Other Marine Organisms.** Fig. 2.6.1a shows the pattern from a cell in the abdominal ganglion of Aplysia [Str-1]. In contrast to the previous example, in this case the oscillator seems to consist of a single unit since temporary blocking of the pulses by membrane hyperpelariation causes a phase shifting in the pattern. An interesting feature of this neuron is that the distribution of the time intervals between pulses has a parabolic form, and thus this cell has been called a *parabolic burster*. Furthermore the number of spikes per minute shows additional rhythms which we shall discuss later. Similar phenomena have been reported by many investigators [Arv-1, Chal-1, Gwi-1, Jac-1, Jac-2, Jac-3, Mat-1, Mend-1, etc.].

Some of the salient features of these oscillations can be described in terms of the dynamics of the nerve membrane. There are many studies and mathematical models describing them, and the Hodgkin–Huxley equations are prominent among them. However, many features of the macroscopic behavior can be deduced by simplified models and this has been a common practice [Har-1, Har-2, Dun-1, Dun-2, Dun-3, Dun-4, Pav-1, Pav-2, Pos-1, Rei-A]. A simple dynamical model of a single neuron can be expressed by the following system:

$$T_0\, dp/dt + p = E \qquad \text{if} \quad p \leqslant R \tag{2.6.1}$$

If $p = R$, then a pulse is emitted and p is instantaneously reset to zero value. Here p corresponds roughly to membrane potential, R to the excitation threshold, and E is a depolarizing agent. This formalism is close to many of the mathematical and electronic models described in the literature [Har-1, Har-2, Dun-1, Dun-2, Dun-3, Dun-4, Pav-1, Pav-2, Pos-1, Rei-A]. A simple calculation shows that if E is constant and greater than R the model fires at a fixed rate with intervals T given by

$$T = -T_0 \ln(1 - R/E) \tag{2.6.2}$$

Note that T is positive in spite of the minus sign since the logarithm of a quantity less than one is negative. If E is much greater than R, then one can use a series expansion for the logarithm and find that

$$T = T_0 R/E \tag{2.6.3}$$

Suppose now that E is a periodic function of time as shown in Fig. 2.6.2. If a piecewise linear approximation is used for E, then Eq. (2.6.1) can be written as

$$T_0\, dp/dt + p = E_1 t_n + E_1(t - t_n) \qquad \text{if} \quad t_1 < t,\, t_n < t_2$$
$$T_0\, dp/dt + p = E_m \qquad \text{if} \quad t_2 < t < t_3$$
$$T_0\, dp/dt + p = E_m - E_1(t_n - t_3) - E_1(t - t_n) \qquad \text{if} \quad t_3 < t,\, t_n < t_4$$

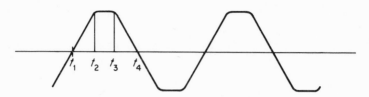

FIG. 2.6.2.   The form of excitation of a neuronal unit which gives rise to a series of parabolic bursts.

where in all cases $p(t_n) = 0$. We have ignored the "corners" of E (at t_2 and t_3) for simplicity. The first equation has as solution

$$p(t) = (E_1 t_n - E_1 T_0)\{1 - \exp[-(t - t_n)/T_0]\} + E_1(t - t_n)$$

The value t_{n+1} when p equals R cannot be found explicitly except by a series expansion of the exponential. Defining $T_n = t_{n+1} - t_n$ and using the first two terms we have

$$T_n = T_0 R/E_1 t_n \tag{2.6.4}$$

For the middle section we have

$$T_n = -T_0 \ln(1 - R/E_m) \tag{2.6.5}$$

and, for the last,

$$T_n = T_0 R/[E_m - E_1(t_n - t_3)] \tag{2.6.6}$$

Although the plot of T_n versus n is not an exact parabola it comes very close to it as can be seen by inspection of Eqs. (2.6.4)–(2.6.6). A complete plot requires special calculations for the intervals near t_1 and t_4 as well as the corners, and it is shown in Fig. 2.6.3.

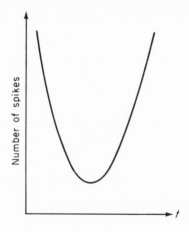

FIG. 2.6.3.   Distribution of interspike intervals in a parabolic burst as modeled by Eqs. (2.6.4), (2.6.5), and (2.6.6).

Thus in a sense a "parabolic" burst is characteristic of a "sinosoidal" variation in the depolarizing input.

The assumption of such a depolarizing waveform could not account for the locust flying control pattern since there a small number of pulses (one or two) tend to be concentrated in an interval much shorter than a period. If we search for the form of E to produce that pattern we reach one which has peaks of rather short duration, as shown in Fig. 2.6.4a and b for the patterns of Fig. 2.6.1b and c, respectively.

a

FIG. 2.6.4. Waveforms of membrane excitation for generating the pulse patterns shown in Fig. 2.6.1b and c.

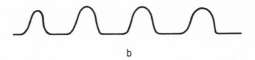

b

Experience with most types of nonlinear oscillators indicates that a change in parameters which results in an increase in amplitude results in a decrease in frequency [Pav-1]. Thus this waveform is rather atypical. Furthermore the form of the peaks suggests that they can be considered as the output of a low-pass filter driven by the pulses which are the output of the neuron. These observations point out the possibility that the oscillator consists of a loop of units each exiting the other as shown in Fig. 2.6.5a. However, an analysis of such a system shows that it is an unstable oscillator and one must assume some inhibitory corrections as well, as shown in Fig. 2.6.5b. One can find in the literature results of computer simulation of such models [Pav-1, Pav-2, Pos-1].

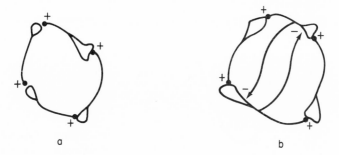

a   b

FIG. 2.6.5. Diagrams of neuronal networks with oscillatory response.

A common feature of all models of this kind is that the resulting periods of oscillation are determined to a large extent by synaptic delays, and therefore they cannot be much longer than the order of magnitude of these delays. In the case of the locust flying system or other high-frequency neural oscillators, this poses no problems since interspike intervals are less than 100 msec. Generally it is unreasonable to expect that such neuronal networks could produce oscillations of much longer periods.

On the other hand, biochemical processes may produce longer period oscillations and, if these are used as a depolarizing agent as shown in Fig. 2.6.2, then neural oscillations of similar periods can be generated. However, in this case the nervous system serves as a transducer rather than as a generator of the oscillations. Thus it does not seem advisable to search for the controller of the circadian or other long-period oscillations in locomotor activity in the interaction among units of the nervous system. It is more likely that the periodicity is generated at a subcellular level as is the case with the parabolic burster.

As mentioned earlier, the parabolic burster is modulated by additional rhythms: in particular, by a circadian and a fortnight lunar. Integration of the number of spikes emitted per 20 min, say, shows distinct peaks following closely the start of the subjective day. The time difference between the maximum and the start of the day shows a fortnight rhythm [Str-1]. This suggests the possibility of a complex oscillatory system where a wide range of frequencies are produced as harmonics or subharmonics of a fundamental oscillation.

In conclusion we should mention that macroscopic oscillations of the neuromuscular system are well known and their descriptions can be found in the literature [Sta-A, Boum-1, Ste-1, etc.].

2.7 Oscillations in Cultures of Fungi

Fungi grown in a proper culture medium may not do so uniformly but instead develop nonuniform patterns with zones of intense growth alternating with areas of slow growth. Figure 2.7.1 shows some typical patterns. It is beyond our scope to give a detailed description of the phenomenon; for this the reader is referred to the literature [Jer-1, Bour-1]. We point out only that the zonation patterns actually reflect time patterns. Indeed when a culture grows out of an original spore the "front" alternates between "slow" and "intense" growth with a more or less fixed time interval elapsing between switching from one growth mode into another. The form and properties of these patterns depend

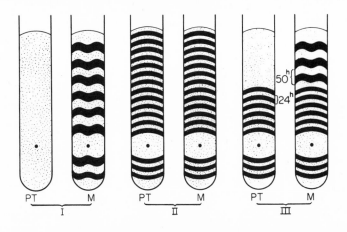

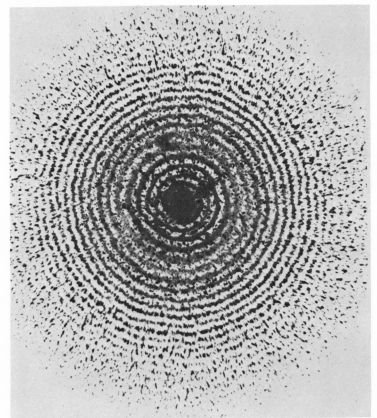

FIG. 2.7.1. Examples of zonation patterns in fungi cultures (top from Jerebzoff [Jer-1]; bottom from Bourrett *et al.* [Bour-1]).

on a number of factors. In particular, certain species of fungi show zonation only when exposed to periodic light and temperature stimuli while other species seem to pocess endogenous rhythms. The growth medium also affects the appearance of zones. Some species present a period which is independent of temperature while in others the period shows a strong temperature dependence. Often the period length is about 24 hours, but periods as long as 7 days and some as low as a few hours have been observed [Jer-1].

This wide variety of rhythmic behavior and the possibility of its chemical manipulation make fungi an interesting subject for research in biological oscillations. However, research in the field has been rather limited, probably because of the lack of impressive practical applications.

In Chapter 8 we will describe certain approaches to analyze the various zonation patterns in terms of the theory of groups of coupled oscillators.

CHAPTER 3

Phase Shifts and Phase Response Curves

3.1 Introduction

When one starts to study oscillatory phenomena in biology he faces a distinctly different situation than in engineering and the physical sciences. There, oscillators are, more often than not, described by their mathematical equations. Whatever ambiguities may exist in the description of an oscillator in an engineering environment, they are usually confined in the value of parameters or the precise functional form of nonlinearities. The state variables are almost always well defined and measurable. Thus assessing the state of an oscillator at any given time is not a major problem. In contrast, the study of most biological oscillators is subject to the following constraints:

(i)   The state variables are not known.
(ii) Even if they are known, they are not measurable.
(iii) The mathematical equations describing the dynamics are not available.

The only thing that is usually known is the time of occurrence of an event which is assumed to be triggered by the oscillator. A well-known example is the start of menstruation. Other examples, as we have seen in the previous chapter, involve the start of locomotor activity by caged animals, the occurrence of a neural pulse in an axon, etc. Even if a continuously varying variable can be measured, it is usually connected only indirectly to the oscillator. Such an example is the sensitivity to drugs or the intensity of locomotor activity, both of which are rather difficult to measure.

This fact has contributed significantly to discussions about the very existence of biological oscillators. Many people have argued that the periodicity of a phenomenon could be attributed to an external periodic stimulus; in other words, to a nonbiological oscillator. Geophysical oscillators have been offered as candidates for such a function.

In view of this situation, it seems important to establish a procedure for assaying the state of an oscillator (even imperfectly) and also for deciding whether the observed periodic behavior is *endogenous* (controlled by a biological oscillator in the organism itself) or *exogenous* (controlled by an oscillator outside the organism).

Such an estimate is provided by the *phase* of the oscillator as determined in relation to the times that its state enters certain regions of the state space. We will give precise definitions in the next section, but we first illustrate this concept by a simple example.

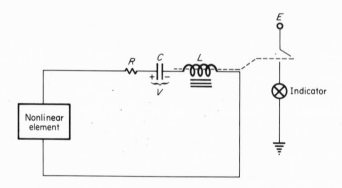

FIG. 3.1.1.   A simple electronic oscillatory circuit.

Figure 3.1.1 shows an electronic circuit where a nonlinear element with characteristic

$$e = KI^3 - R'I$$

is included. If I is the current flow through the circuit and V the voltage drop across the capacitor, then the following equations describe the system:

$$dV/dt = (1/C)I \tag{3.1.1}$$

$$dI/dt = -(1/L)V + (1/L)(rI - KI^3) \tag{3.1.2}$$

where $r = R' - R > 0$. These equations can be derived easily by an application of Kirchoff's second law. The reader will probably recognize the van der Pol oscillator written in a nonstandard form.

The inductor can be thought of as the coils of a relay which is activated any time the value of the current is greater than I_0 amps in absolute value. The relay is deactivated when the absolute value of the current drops below I_1. By recording the times the relay opens and closes one obtains an estimate of the value of current then. If the system operates on a limit cycle, then the value of the voltage can also be found. Here we have four timing events per cycle. If the relay has a bias (via an external coil), then it may close only when the current I exceeds a positive value I_0'. Then the times when the relay closes will indicate that $I = I_0'$. If T is the period of the oscillations, then the phase of the system could be defined as the time since the last closing of the relay was observed. This quantity would allow determining the state of the system uniquely if we also knew that the latter was on the limit cycle (steady state oscillations). If the system is not on the limit cycle, then the phase would not be meaningful, although one could still observe relay closings.

In biological terms one can think of a biochemical oscillator where, once the concentration of a substance exceeds a certain level, then a chain of reactions (independent of the oscillator) is initiated, and that time can be estimated by observing their results. (See Section 3.6.)

One could attempt to obtain an estimate of the structure of the system by perturbing it; for example, by instantaneously short circuiting the capacitor. This will delay or advance the next timing event by a certain amount of time. If these times are known as functions of the times the short circuit occurred, they will provide some information about the circuit. The plot of this function can be obtained experimentally in biological oscillators and it has been the subject of extensive research.

It is commonly known as a phase response curve for a given stimulus.

In the next section we will introduce certain formal definitions and proceed to study the formal properties of phase response curves.

3.2 Timing Sequences, Isochrones, Phase Response Curves, and Phase Transition Curves

We introduce here certain formal definitions which will be useful in the sequence.

Let L denote a limit cycle of a dynamical system and let $R(L)$ be its region of attraction. Suppose now that a surface B divides $R(L)$ into two parts A_1 and A_2 and that L intersects B in exactly two points. Typically, B will represent a threshold with respect to one of the state variables. Let now $J(\mathbf{x}, t)$ be a trajectory starting at a state $\mathbf{x}$ at time t:

DEFINITION 3.2.1. The *timing sequence* of a state $\mathbf{x}$ is defined as the sequence of times t_1, t_2,..., t_n,... when $J(\mathbf{x}, 0)$ crosses B by going from A_1 into A_2. We denote it by

$$TS(\mathbf{x}) = \{t_1, t_2,..., t_n,...\} \tag{3.2.1}$$

Obviously there are cases when $TS(\mathbf{x})$ is empty (for example, if $\mathbf{x}$ is a stable singularity). In the electronic circuit example the timing sequence of a given initial state $I(0)$, $V(0)$ can be the times when the relay closes.

If T is the period of the oscillation on the limit cycle, then the following are two obvious results:

PROPOSITION 3.2.1:   (a) If $\mathbf{x} \in L$, then

$$t_{k+1} - t_k = T \quad \text{for all} \quad t_k \in TS(\mathbf{x})$$

(b) If $\mathbf{x} \in R(L)$, then

$$\lim_{k \to \infty} |\, t_{k+1} - t_k \,| = T \quad \text{for all} \quad t_k \in TS(\mathbf{x})$$

If two states are on the limit cycle, then their phase difference is easily definable as the difference between two elements of their timing sequences modulo T. For states outside the limit cycle this is not as easy. One way to do it is the following:

Let $\mathbf{x} \in L$ have a timing sequence $TS(\mathbf{x})$. We may now consider all other points in the state space with the same timing sequence.

DEFINITION 3.2.2. An *isochrone* [Win-2, Win-3] is defined as the set $I(\mathbf{x})$ of all points whose timing sequence tends to $TS(\mathbf{x})$ for $\mathbf{x} \in L$ in the following manner:

If $t_k \in TS(\mathbf{y})$ and $t_j' \in TS(\mathbf{x})$, then

$$\lim_{k,j \to \infty} |\, t_k - t_j' \,|_{\mathrm{mod}\,T} = 0$$

i.e.,

$$I(\mathbf{x}) = \{\mathbf{y} \mid TS(\mathbf{y}) \to TS(\mathbf{x})\} \tag{3.2.2}$$

The following are direct consequences of the definition:

PROPOSITION 3.2.2:   (a) If $\mathbf{y} \in L$, then it cannot belong to the isochrone of $\mathbf{x} \in L$ if $\mathbf{x} \neq \mathbf{y}$.

(b) If $\mathbf{y}$ is a singularity, then it cannot belong to any isochrone.

(c) If $\mathbf{y}$ is an unstable singularity surrounded by a limit cycle L, then it is a limit point of all the isochrones associated with L.

(d) No two isochrones can intersect each other (of course they can have common limit points).

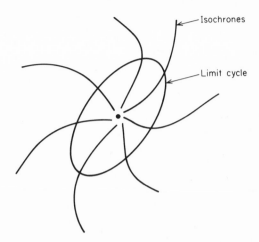

FIG. 3.2.1. A sketch of the topology of the isochrones and the limit cycle of a dynamical system.

Figure 3.2.1 shows a simple example of isochrones.

Now we are able to define the phase difference between any two points:

DEFINITION 3.2.3. The *phase difference* between two points $\mathbf{y}_1$ and $\mathbf{y}_2$ is defined as follows:

(a) If $\mathbf{y}_1 \in L$ and $\mathbf{y}_2 \in L$, then

$$P(\mathbf{y}_1 , \mathbf{y}_2) = (t_k - t_j)_{\mathrm{mod}\,T} \qquad t_k \in TS(\mathbf{y}_1), \quad t_j \in TS(\mathbf{y}_2)$$

(b) Otherwise let $\mathbf{x}_1 \in L$ and $\mathbf{x}_2 \in L$ be such that $y_1 \in I(\mathbf{x}_1)$ and $\mathbf{y}_2 \in I(\mathbf{x}_2)$. Then

$$P(\mathbf{y}_1 , \mathbf{y}_2) = P(\mathbf{x}_1 , \mathbf{x}_2)$$

This definition allows the experimental measurement of phase differences of any two states. Indeed all we need to do is start two "cultures" at different states, wait till the oscillations reach the limit cycle, and then measure the phase difference.

Let us now assign to a point $\mathbf{z}$ of the limit cycle "absolute" phase zero and let us define the *phase of a point* as its phase difference from $\mathbf{z}$.

DEFINITION 3.2.4. Let S be an input of duration T_s applied to the system when its state is at $\mathbf{x} \in L$. Let $\mathbf{y}$ be the state right after the removal of S and let $\mathbf{x}' \in L$ be the state where the system would have been at that time if S had not been applied at all. In other words, $\mathbf{x}'$ is defined from the relation

$$P(\mathbf{x}, \mathbf{x}') = T_s + kT, \qquad k \quad \text{an integer} \tag{3.2.3}$$

Then the *phase shift* $Q(\mathbf{x}, S)$ *caused by* S applied at $\mathbf{x}$ is defined as the phase difference $P(\mathbf{x}', \mathbf{y})$ if $\mathbf{y} \in R(L)$. If $\mathbf{y} \notin R(L)$, then the phase shift is undefined.

If the duration of S is a small fraction of the period (e.g., 10 min versus 24 hours), then the distinction between $\mathbf{x}$ and $\mathbf{x}'$ is diminished and the phase shift could be defined as $P(\mathbf{x}, \mathbf{y})$ without significant error.

DEFINITION 3.2.5.   The *phase response curve* (PRC) *for* S is defined as the plot of the phase shift $Q(\mathbf{x}, S)$ versus the phase of $\mathbf{x}$ [i.e., $P(\mathbf{x}, \mathbf{z})$].

Note that if $\mathbf{x} \notin L$ the above two definitions are meaningless since the effect of S may vary along an isochrone.

Some generalizations about the shape of the phase response curves can be stated. Because of the continuity of dynamical systems they are expected to be continuous curves, except for "jumps" of size T introduced by the modulo operation in the definition of phase difference. The number of their zeros equals the number of points $\mathbf{x}$ of L which are moved by S on the isochrone of $\mathbf{x}'$ as defined by Eq. (3.2.3) (or in special cases are not moved at all). They may also have an infinite number of zeros if there are regions where S has the above effect. We will refer to such regions as *zero intervals*. Thus the PRC of Fig. 3.2.2 has one isolated zero and one zero interval. If one plots a PRC from 0 to T [the values of $P(\mathbf{x}, z)$], then both its end points must have the same value (they both correspond to $\mathbf{z}$) and therefore the curve must have *an even number of zeros, either isolated or intervals, or else present discontinuities*. In either case we have

PROPOSITION 3.2.3.   The total number of isolated zeros, zero intervals, and jumps of size T of a phase response curve must be even.

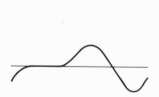

FIG. 3.2.2.   A PRC with a zero interval and one isolated zero.

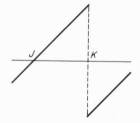

FIG. 3.2.3.   A linear PRC produced by a stimulus which always brings the state of the system to a fixed isochrone.

This is probably the only general statement that one can make about the shape of phase response curves. Some additional special cases are discussed next.

PROPOSITION 3.2.4. If the input S leaves always the state of the system at the same isochrone J, then the PRC will be linear with slope one and with one jump. Its zero will correspond to the intersection of J with the limit cycle L.

Proof. Let **y** be the intersection of J and L. Then, because of Definitions 3.2.3a and 3.2.4,

$$Q(\mathbf{x}, S) = P(\mathbf{x}', \mathbf{y}) = [P(\mathbf{x}', \mathbf{x}) + P(\mathbf{x}, \mathbf{z}) + P(\mathbf{z}, \mathbf{y})] \bmod T \quad (3.2.4)$$

Since the first and last terms are fixed, the plot of $P(\mathbf{x}', \mathbf{y})$ vs $P(\mathbf{x}, \mathbf{z})$ will be a parallel shift of the plot of $P(\mathbf{x}, \mathbf{z})$ vs $P(\mathbf{x}, \mathbf{z})$.

Figure 3.2.3 illustrates this case.

PROPOSITION 3.2.5. If no point **x** of L is mapped by S on an isochrone corresponding to a point **v** of the limit cycle which is such that the time required to reach **x** from **v** is greater than $T/2$ for a phase delay or less than $T/2$ for a phase advance, then the PRC will have no discontinuities.

Proof. The hypothesis implies that during the computation of the phase difference no use of the modulo T operation will be made. Since the latter is the only cause for discontinuities there will be none.

In general, PCR's are maps of L into itself: Indeed suppose that S moves **x** to **y**. Assume for simplicity that $\mathbf{x} \simeq \mathbf{x}'$. Let $\mathbf{y}'$ be the intersection of L and the isochrone where **y** belongs. Then $P(\mathbf{x}, \mathbf{y}') = P(\mathbf{x}, \mathbf{y})$ and S maps **x** into $\mathbf{y}'$. Points of zero phase shift correspond to fixed points of this mapping. Discontinuities correspond to mapping a point into another $T/2$ time units apart along the limit cycle. Figure 3.2.4 shows the mapping corresponding to the PRC shown in Fig. 3.2.3. Obviously one can always deduce such a mapping from a given PRC.

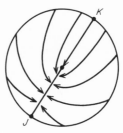

FIG. 3.2.4. A mapping of a limit cycle into itself deduced from the PRC of Fig. 3.2.3.

However this is not the case with the state space mapping induced by S. The latter problem is insufficiently defined in general.

The only special case when the latter mapping can be deduced from the PRC is *when S transfers the state of the system on or very near to L.* Then this mapping is closely related to the mapping of L into itself. When this is true the PRC can be used for a thorough dynamical investigation of the system. Given a physical system one would like to know whether this is the case. The way to find out is based on the observation that in this case a superposition law holds for the PRC. If S is applied twice, then the final phase shift can be predicted by applying twice the mapping suggested by the PRC. If this prediction agrees with the observation for many points of L, then one can be reasonably sure that the original assumption is correct. This and other points will be discussed fully after we give some examples of PRC's obtained experimentally.

The effect of a stimulus can also be expressed through a phase transition curve.

DEFINITION 3.2.6. Let S be an input of duration T_s applied to the system when its state is at $\mathbf{x} \in L$ and let $\mathbf{y}$ be the state after the removal of S. Then the *phase transition curve (PTC) for S* is defined as the plot of the phase of $\mathbf{y}$ [i.e., $P(\mathbf{y}, \mathbf{z})$] minus T_s versus the phase of $\mathbf{x}$ [i.e., $P(\mathbf{x}, \mathbf{z})$].

If $f(p)$ denotes the function describing a PRC (p is the phase) and $g(p)$ the function describing a PTC for the same stimulus, the two functions are related by

$$g(p) = [p + f(p)]_{\mathrm{mod}\,T} \qquad (3.2.5)$$

A number of obvious properties about the shape of PTC's can be deduced from similar properties of PRC's.

Finally we look into one more alternative definition.

DEFINITION 3.2.7. The *cophase* [Win-2, Win-3] associated with an input S is defined as the time interval between the application of S and the next occurrence of the time event (modulo T).

PROPOSITION 3.2.6. The plot of the cophase θ versus the phase when S is applied is a complement of the corresponding PTC.

Proof. Let $\mathbf{x}_0$ be the state of the system when the timing event occurs and let q be its phase; i.e.,

$$q = P(\mathbf{x}_0, \mathbf{z})$$

Let $g(p)$ be the "new" phase caused by an application of S at p. If S had caused no phase shift [i.e., $g(p) = p$], then the next timing event would occur at time

$$T + q - p$$

after the application of S. If $g(p) \neq 0$, then the phase at the end of S will be $g(p) + T_s$ instead of $p + T_s$. Thus the above expression should be corrected by adding the term

$$p - g(p)$$

or

$$\theta = [q - g(p)]_{\mathrm{mod}\, T}$$

In the sequence we will concentrate on PRC's since the other two formulations are equivalent.

According to our definitions positive phase shifts correspond to phase "advances" while negative phase shifts to phase "delays." On the other hand, in the literature PRC's are usually plotted with delays upwards and advances downwards. We will follow this notation for the sake of consistency with the traditional form.

3.3 Experimental Phase Response Curves

In the previous section we pointed out some general properties of PRC's. It turns out that most curves obtained experimentally belong to a small subset of all possible shapes of PRC's. Here will examine some examples of such curves, all but one of which are from circadian rhythms.

Figure 3.3.1 shows the PRC of the phototactic response rhythm of a unicellular organism (*Euglena gracilis*) when the stimulus was pulses of light of 4 hours duration [Fel-1].

In this and the following examples the subject was first exposed to a stimulus consisting of 12 hours of light given every 24 hours. Then it was allowed to free run in complete dark. The phase reference point z (0 absissa) was taken to correspond to the start of the light period (strictly speaking, it is the time obtained by adding multiples of 24 hours to the last time the 12-hour light period was initiated). Thus the parts of the limit cycle between 0 and 12 might be said to correspond to the *subjective day* while the rest correspond to the *subjective night*. In this sense the phase measured in hours can be said to constitute a *subjective time*. The organism functions roughly as though it was exposed to a 24-hour photoperiodic regime with 12 hours light followed by 12 hours dark. Quite often the term *circadian time* (CT) is used instead of subjective time. We summarize these remarks in the following definition:

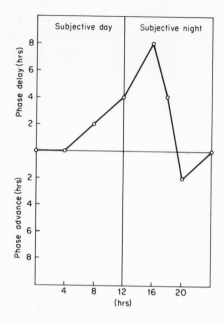

FIG. 3.3.1. PRC of the phototactic response of the alga
Euglena [Fel-1].

DEFINITION 3.3.1. Circadian time (or subjective time) is the phase difference $P(\mathbf{x}, \mathbf{z})$ measured in hours where $\mathbf{z}$ is taken to be that point of the limit cycle where the last 12-hour photoperiod, seen by the subject, was initiated.

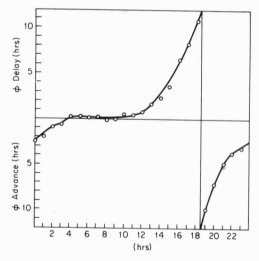

FIG. 3.3.2. PRC for light pulses (100 f-c) of 15 min duration for the rhythm of emergence of fruitflies (*Drosophila pseudoobscura*) [Pit-5].

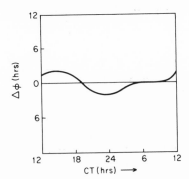

FIG. 3.3.3. As Fig. 3.3.2 but for light pulses of 30 sec duration [Win-3].

Figure 3.3.2 shows the PRC of the rhythm of pupal eclosion in *Drosophila pseudoobscura* (a species of fruitflies). The stimulus *S* consisted of 15 min of white fluorescent light with 100 f-c intensity [Pit-5].

Figure 3.3.3 shows a similar curve where the duration of stimulus was only 30 sec [Win-3].

Figure 3.3.4 shows the PRC of the locomotor rhythm (activity onset) of a hamster, *Mesocricetus auratus. S* consisted of 10 min of white light [DeC-2]. Curves for two individuals are shown.

Figure 3.3.5 shows the PRC of the leaf movement of a coleus plant. *S* consisted of 3 hours of light [Hal-4].

Finally, Fig. 3.3.6 shows the PRC of the same rhythm as Fig. 3.3.2 but with *S* being 12 hours long [Pit-3].

The similarity among all these PRC's is rather striking in view of the wide difference among the rhythms and organisms involved. It also

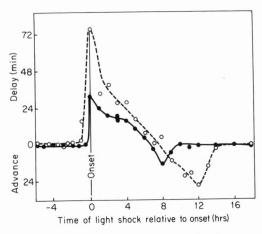

FIG. 3.3.4. PRC for light pulses of 10 min duration for the locomotor rhythm of a hamster [DeC-2].

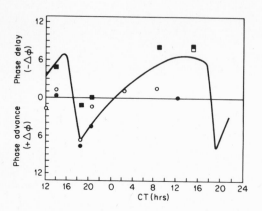

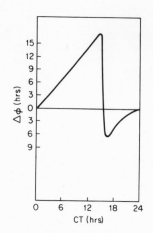

FIG. 3.3.5. PRC for light pulses of 3 hr duration for the leaf movement rhythm of a coleus plant [Hal-4]: (■) blue, (●) red, (○) far red (FR), (□) blue + FR.

FIG. 3.3.6. Same as Fig. 3.3.2 but for light pulses of 12 hr duration [Pit-3].

seems that PRC's corresponding to stimuli of long duration resemble more the shape of Fig. 3.2.3.

However it is not difficult to make a case that all these PRC's have exactly the shape required by their requirement for adjustment in a photoperiodic environment: If the organism sees light during its subjective day it should not react to it in any significant way. If it sees light early in its subjective night it should delay its rhythm, and if it sees light late during its subjective night it should advance its rhythm. Thus the general shape of a PRC will not necessarily give us any substantial information about the structure of the oscillator regulating the rhythmic activity.

However a more detailed study of PRC's can be more fruitful. In particular we will show that, under certain conditions, the knowledge of the PRC for a particular stimulus allows the prediction of the response of the organism to other stimuli.

Figure 3.3.7 shows a PRC for a rhythm of a very different kind [Pye-4]. The oscillations under consideration were those of DPNH in a cell-free extract of yeast. Their period is about 5 min. The input was the addition of small amounts of ADP. The effect of this addition is always instantaneous and, after a small fraction of the period, the oscillation resumes its regular waveform. Thus it may be safely assumed that, although phenomenologically the input is a step function, in reality it is of very short duration because ADP is consumed in the chemical

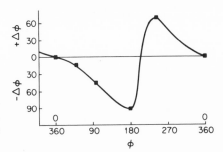

FIG. 3.3.7. PRC for the addition of ADP in all of the oscillations of DPNH in a cell-free extract of yeast [Pye-4].

processes of the yeast culture. (This does not necessarily mean that ADP is one of the state variables.) The shape of this PRC is still quite similar to those of Figs. 3.3.1–3.3.5, different as their origins might be.

3.4 Analysis of Phase Response Curves

Let $f(p)$ denote the phase shift produced by S when applied at a point with phase p (phase difference from z). The state of the system will eventually reach a point on L with phase q given by the equation

$$q = \{p + f(p)\} \bmod T \qquad (3.4.1)$$

This is the equation of the PTC. If the last assumption of Section 3.2 holds, then q is achieved instantaneously. Then applying the input S twice will result in a new phase Q given by

$$Q = \{q + t + f(q + t)\} \bmod T \qquad (3.4.2)$$

or

$$Q = \{p + f(p) + t + f[p + f(p) + t]\} \bmod T \qquad (3.4.2')$$

where t is the time between the two starts of application of S. (It is assumed that the duration of S is less than t.) Equation (3.4.2′) is not expected to hold in general because the effect of S will be different at various points of an isochrone.

It turns out that this superposition is indeed valid for some rhythms. Experimental verification of the fact consists of agreement between prediction of the effect of multiple stimuli [by Eq. (3.4.2)] and observation. This in combination with the fact that light stimuli of short duration have virtually no effect during the subjective day provides a description for the mapping of L into itself caused by such stimuli. Figure 3.4.1a shows a simple example of such a mapping together with the corresponding phase response curve.

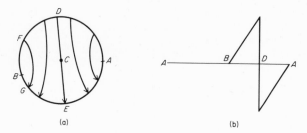

FIG. 3.4.1.   (a) Mapping of limit cycle into itself deduced from a (b) PRC.

Suppose now that a stimulus of longer duration is used such that, when applied on a point (e.g., *F* in Fig. 3.4.1a), it moves it to a new state (*G*), and by the time it reaches the start of subjective night *B* the stimulus is still present. This will move it back to the zone *BEA* and, for all practical purposes, the effect will be to keep the state at *B* as long as *S* is present. If the duration of *S* is longer than that of *AB*, then *S* will map all points of the limit cycle onto *B* and a PRC of the form shown in Fig. 3.4.2 is to be expected. The similarity between this and the PRC of Fig. 3.3.5 is obvious (also between Fig. 3.4.1b and Fig. 3.3.2).

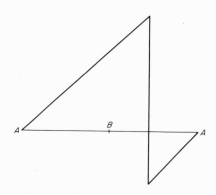

FIG. 3.4.2.   PRC for a stimulus of long duration. It is derived from the data of Fig. 3.4.1.

Thus the fruitfly clock seems to be affected by light according to a mapping similar to the one shown in Fig. 3.4.1 [Pit-7, Pav-3]. The examination of the PRC's has indeed given us some information about the circadian clock.

On the basis of this model one could derive the PRC's for stimuli of various durations from the PRC's to a stimulus of short duration. This has indeed been done in the case of the eclosion rhythm of Drosophila pseudoobscura.

The next question is how one can predict the effect of stimuli shorter than the one for which a phase response curve of the kind shown in

Fig. 3.4.1 was obtained. In the limit, when no stimulus at all is applied, there will be no phase shifts at all; thus, in between, a "flatter" curve is to be expected. A simple model can be achieved by assuming the isochrones to be straight lines (see Section 3.5 for a justification of this point) and that the mapping shown in Fig. 3.4.1 takes the system part way towards the zone BEA. Figure 3.4.3 illustrates this situation together

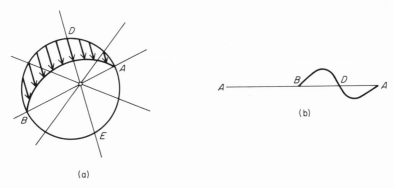

FIG. 3.4.3.   (a) Mapping of the limit cycle into the isochrones by a stimulus of short duration and (b) the corresponding PRC.

with the corresponding PRC. In this case the PRC is of the type shown in Figs. 3.3.3 and 3.3.4 as well as the PRC for the fruitfly rhythm obtained for stimuli of duration of less than 50 sec.

We thus have an interesting observation: the PRC's of various organisms present a remarkably close resemblance among them, especially if one compares PRC's corresponding to stimuli of different durations (e.g., 50 sec for the fruitflies and 10 min for the rodents). Furthermore the model of Fig. 3.4.3 seems to be universal! The fact that different durations have the same effect on different rhythms can be easily explained by assuming different sensitivities to light.

We will see in subsequent chapters some other uses of the PRC. However, first we would like to look back at the electronic circuit of Fig. 3.3.1 and attempt to describe its isochrones and phase response curves.

3.5   Isochrones and Phase Response Curves of a van der Pol Oscillator

The circuit of Fig. 3.1.1 represents a van der Pol oscillator. This has been analyzed in Section 1.5, and we have seen that the amplitude a

and phase ψ satisfy the following conditions [Eqs. (1.5.18) and (1.5.25)]:

$$d\psi/dt = \omega \tag{3.5.1}$$

$$da/dt = (\varepsilon a/2)(1 - a^2/4) \tag{3.5.2}$$

The first equation indicates that the isochrones are approximately straight lines. The motion is approximated by

$$x(t) = a \cos \psi \tag{3.5.3}$$

where a and ψ are given by (3.5.1) and (3.5.2). Then the trajectory is of helicoidal form in the $(x, dx/dt)$ [or (J, V)] plane (Fig. 3.5.1). This

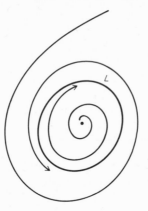

Fig. 3.5.1.   Sketch of the trajectories of a van der Pol oscillator on the phase plane.

would be also true for any isoperiodic oscillator (as defined in Section 1.5). Discharging the capacitor corresponds to setting $V = 0$ (and keeping it there). Thus the mapping and the corresponding PRC should be of the forms shown in Fig. 3.5.2. The latter is unlike any observed in circadian rhythms. On the other hand, consider Fig. 3.5.3 and assume that the

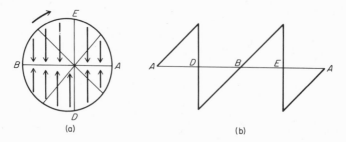

(a)   (b)

Fig. 3.5.2.   (a) Mapping of the limit cycle into the isochrones induced by short circuiting the capacitor of the circuit of Fig. 3.1.1; (b) the corresponding PRC.

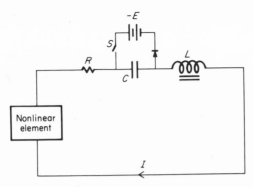

FIG. 3.5.3. An electronic oscillatory circuit for producing PRC's.

effect of the "stimulus" is to close the switch S. Then while S is closed V is clamped at the value $-E_0$ if $V > -E_0$ and the mapping and the corresponding PRC are of the form shown in Fig. 3.5.4, which looks closer to the ones obtained experimentally. If E_0 is taken equal to zero, then the mapping and PRC are shown in Fig. 3.5.5.

These attempts at "modeling," however, should be kept in proper

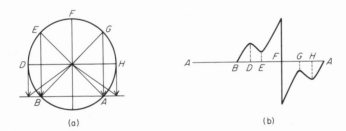

FIG. 3.5.4. (a) Mapping of the limit cycle into the isochrones obtained by closing the switch S in the circuit of Fig. 3.5.3; (b) the corresponding PRC.

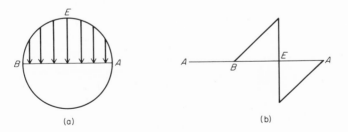

FIG. 3.5.5. Same as Fig. 3.5.4 except that $E_0 = 0$.

perspective. They are given simply as an illustration of the physical significance of the mappings discussed in this chapter.

Another example closer to biology will be discussed next.

3.6 Phase Response Curves of a Biochemical Oscillator

We will show now an example of phase response curves obtained from a biochemical oscillator. The following set of reactions describe such a system [Hig-2, Pav-9]:

$$G \xrightarrow{1} X \tag{a}$$

$$X + E_1{}^+ \xrightarrow{2} E_1 X \xrightarrow{3} E_1 + Y \tag{b}$$

$$Y + E_1 \underset{5}{\overset{4}{\rightleftharpoons}} E_1{}^+ \tag{c}$$

$$Y + E_2 \xrightarrow{6} E_2 Y \xrightarrow{7} E_2 + Z \tag{d}$$

X is a substrate, Y is an activator, E_1 and E_2 are enzymes ($E_1{}^+$ being an active form of E_1), G is a substance in constant supply (at least under ordinary conditions) which is transformed into X according to Reaction (a), and Z is the final product. X is transformed into Y in an enzyme-catalyzed reaction (b), obeying the Michaelis–Menten law. Y then is transformed into Z by a similar reaction (d). Reaction (c) describes the activation of E_1 by Y. One possible physical mechanism for achieving this result is a ligand-induced conformation change or allosteric effect. Since one cannot have sustained oscillations without some form of feedback, Reaction (c) is very important in this model because it provides precisely that feedback.

It can be shown that the chemical kinetics of this set of reactions are described by the following equations:

$$dx/dt = k_1 g - v \tag{3.6.1}$$

$$dy/dt = v - k_7 e_2 y/[y + (k_y/k_6)] \tag{3.6.2}$$

where

$$v = \frac{k_3 e_1 xy}{y[x + (k_3/k_2)] + (k_3/k_2)(k_4/k_5)} \tag{3.6.3}$$

In the above equations lower case letters denote the concentrations of the corresponding substances. Here e_1 is the total concentration of E_1 in both active and inactive forms, while e_2 is the concentration of the active form only of E_2 (either free or bound); k_i denotes the rate constant of the ith reaction. In the derivation of the expression for v it has also been assumed that Reaction (c) reaches chemical equilibrium much faster than the other reactions (this will be the case if k_4 and k_5 are much larger than the other rate constants).

There exists evidence that such a system is present in the glycolytic chain with the following physical counterparts for the various substances involved: G corresponds to glucose, X to fructose 6-phosphate, Y to FDP (fructose-diphosphate), E_1 to phosphofructokinase, and E_2 to aldolese. A modification of the above description may identify Y with ADP (adenosine-diphosphate).

It can be shown that for appropriate values of the parameters involved the above system presents self-sustained oscillations with a limit cycle.

A simplification of the above equations can be achieved via a set of substitutions:

$$dx/dt = D - v \tag{3.6.4}$$

$$dy/dt = v - B_2 y/(y + c) \tag{3.6.5}$$

$$v = B_1 xy/[y(x + A_1) + A] \tag{3.6.6}$$

where

$$A = (k_3/k_2)(k_4/k_5), \qquad A_1 = (k_3/k_2)$$

$$B_1 = k_3 e_1, \qquad B_2 = k_7 e_2$$

$$C = (k_7/k_6), \qquad D = k_1 g$$

Let us assume now the existence of an external stimulus which causes a decrease in y. If the stimulus is light this would be the case if Reactions (c) or (d) above were of photochemical nature. The decrease in y can be achieved either through an increase in the coefficient B_2 in Eq. (3.6.5) or through the activation of a new chemical reaction which removes Y and which obeys the Michaelis–Menten law. If k_8 and k_9 are the two rate constants involved, then Eq. (3.6.2) should be modified by the addition of an extra term:

$$\frac{dy}{dt} = v - \frac{k_7 e_2 y}{y + (k_7/k_6)} - \frac{k_9 e_3 y}{y + (k_9/k_8)} \tag{3.6.7}$$

where e_3 is the concentration of the enzyme involved in the new reaction. It may be interpreted as a light-activated enzyme. If it happens that k_9/k_8 equals approximately k_7/k_6, then the last two terms of the above equation can be combined to give an equation identical to Eq. (3.6.5) with B_2 defined now as

$$B_2 = k_7 e_2 + k_9 e_3$$

Therefore under these conditions the two possible mechanisms of light action will be indistinguishable through macroscopic observations.

It should be noted that the topology of the effect of the stimulus resembles now very much the transformations illustrated in Figs. 3.4.1 and 3.4.3. The main difference is that isochrones do not have now the simple geometry illustrated in the last figure.

In order to study this transformation and the corresponding PRC's in more detail one can proceed with a computer simulation of the system of Eqs. (3.6.4)–(3.6.7). Figure 3.6.1 shows the limit cycle plotted

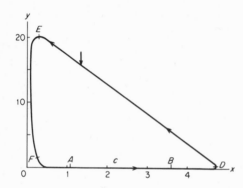

FIG. 3.6.1. Phase plane plot of the normalized system described by Eqs. (3.6.4) and (3.6.5) [Pav-9].

on the x–y plane. Various parts of it correlate with Reactions (a)–(d) as follows.

Zone ABD is characterized by a low concentration of Y, so that Reaction (d) proceeds at a very slow rate, if at all. The behavior of the system in this zone is dictated by Reaction (a) (production of X). Zone DE is characterized by an increase in Y accompanied by a decrease in X. This means that Reactions (b) and (c) are dominant and tend to overshadow (a). Eventually (d) becomes important and it becomes dominant in the zone EFA where Y is transformed into Z.

Thus one expects the application of the stimulus in the zone ABD to have very small or no effect at all in the phase of the oscillation.

During the simulation, the strength of the stimulus is expressed as an increase in the value of B_2. Figures 3.6.2 and 3.6.3 show phase response curves thus obtained. For the sake of comparison the notation of circadian PRC's is used. The first of these figures shows the phase response curves caused by a short pulse. Curve A is for a strong light effect and resembles very closely the 15-min phase response curve of the eclosion rhythm of *Drosophila pseudoobscura* (Fig. 3.3.2). The other curve, B, for a weak-light effect, resembles closely the 10-min phase response curves for rodents (Fig. 3.3.4) and the weak stimulus

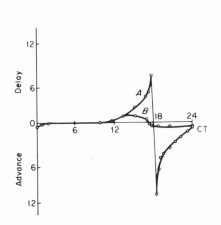

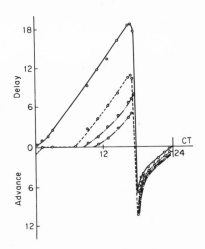

Fig. 3.6.2. Phase response curve for a pulse of about 10 min duration. Curve A (20) is for strong-light effect and Curve B (3) for weak-light effect. All coordinates are in hours [Pav-9].

Fig. 3.6.3. Phase response curves for pulses of various durations and strong-light effect. All coordinates are in hours [Pav-9]. Duration: (———) 12, (---) 6, (–··–) 3, (–·–) 1 hr.

curve for *Drosophila* (Fig. 3.3.3). These results are important because, as we have seen in Section 3.4, any model which simulates successfully the short-pulse phase response curve of an organism will also simulate a large variety of other responses to light. Figure 3.6.3 presents an additional verification by showing the phase response curves for various durations and strong-light effects. They all resemble very closely the corresponding curves of the eclosion rhythm of *Drosophila pseudoobscura* (Fig. 3.3.6).

3.7 Bibliographical Notes

Phase response curves have been used for the study of biological rhythms for a long time. Pittendrigh should be credited with the first systematic exploitation of the information contained in them [Pit-3, Pit-4, Pit-5, Pit-6, Pit-7]. Some of his work will be described in the next two chapters. The formalism of Section 3.2 has been motivated by the works of Ottensen [Ott-1] and, in particular, of Winfree [Win-2, Win-3], who used that framework to design and perform the experiment described in subsequent chapters. The derivation of PRC's of long duration from ones of short duration was first described by Pavlidis [Pav-3]. The biochemical oscillator of Section 3.6 was first described and analyzed by Higgins [Hig-1]. Pavlidis and Kauzman [Pav-9] used it as a model for circadian rhythms and derived the corresponding PRC's. Additional reading on experimental PRC's can be found in the literature [Asc-2, Dec-1, Dec-2, Dec-3, Zim-2], and in the references of Section 3.3.

CHAPTER 4

Entrainment of Oscillators by External Inputs

4.1 Introduction

When a linear oscillatory system is driven by an external periodic input its response contains both frequency components. This is also, in general, true with nonlinear oscillators. However, in this case, if the external frequency is close to the characteristic frequency of the oscillator itself, then it is possible to have a response at the external frequency only. This phenomenon is known as *entrainment* or *synchronization*. It is of paramount importance in biological oscillators because it allows them to "latch on" to the environment. Thus a rhythm with a free-running period of 24.7 hours may be synchronized to 24 hours when exposed to the natural sequence of day and night.

This phenomenon is also significant in technological applications, and for this reason there is considerable literature on the subject. Nevertheless, certain questions related to biological applications have received little coverage.

The following is a brief summary of the problem, assuming that we deal with an oscillator with one degree of freedom which is described by the following equation:

$$d^2x/dt^2 + f(x, dx/dt) + \omega_0^2 x = E \cos \omega_1 t \qquad (4.1.1)$$

If the function f is identically zero, then we deal with a linear system whose solution is of the form

$$x(t) = A \sin \omega_0 t + B \cos \omega_0 t + \frac{E}{\omega_0^2 - \omega_1^2} \cos \omega_1 t \qquad (4.1.2)$$

where A and B are constants depending on the initial conditions.

71

If f is not identically zero, then there exists a set of pairs of values of the amplitude E and the absolute difference in frequencies $\Delta\omega = |\omega_0 - \omega_1|$ such that the output of the system contains only the frequency ω_1. Figure 4.1.1 illustrates a typical example. Entrainment occurs in the shaded part of the plane.

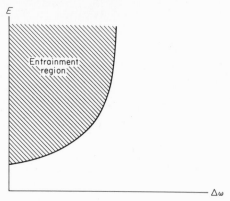

FIG. 4.1.1. Illustration of the relation between the amplitude E of the external input and the difference in frequencies $\Delta\omega$ which produces entrainment of a nonlinear oscillator.

What happens when the values of E and $\Delta\omega$ are below the line but close to it? In general there is a rich variety of possible responses, usually characterized by the fact that both ω_0 and ω_1 are present. In the case that $\Delta\omega = 0$ but E is very small the phase of the oscillation is not influenced by the input. If ω_1 is close to an integral multiple of ω_0, then it is possible to have *subharmonic entrainment* at the corresponding fraction of ω_1. If $\Delta\omega$ and E are close to the boundary one can observe *beats* with frequency $\Delta\omega$.

The study of biological oscillators has revealed that not only can they be entrained by periodic changes in their environment (which is not surprising at all) but they also show dependence of the limits of entrainment on the amplitude of the input, subharmonic entrainment, beats, etc. Thus one has a very beautiful correspondence between properties of oscillators derived by abstract mathematical analysis and experimental observations. Describing this close correspondence will be the subject of this chapter. We will alternate our discussion between mathematical analyses and descriptions of experimental results.

We will start in the next section with a rather simple case, the entrainment of a van der Pol oscillator. It turns out that the behavior of such a system exemplifies most of the salient features of nonlinear entrainment.

The results of this analysis are applicable to the behavior of biological rhythms under gradual changes in their environment. The effect of trains of pulses as entraining agents will be discussed next, and illustrations of a very close agreement between theoretical and experimental results will be given.

4.2 Entrainment of a van der Pol Oscillator

The van der Pol oscillator has been analyzed extensively in the technical literature (see also Section 1.5) and here we will use it to illustrate a method for studying entrainment. Our presentation is a condensation of the development usually found in the mathematical literature [And-I, But-I, Haa-I, Min-I].

We start with the usual equation but with a nonzero right-hand side:

$$d^2x/dt^2 - \varepsilon(1 - x^2)\,dx/dt + \omega_0^2 x = E \cos \omega_1 t \qquad (4.2.1)$$

It will be convenient in the subsequent analysis to consider the Rayleigh form, which results by integrating both sides of Eq. (4.2.1) with respect to time and defining

$$v(t) = \int_0^t x(t)\,dt$$

Then Eq. (4.2.1) becomes

$$d^2v/dt^2 - \varepsilon[dv/dt - \tfrac{1}{3}(dv/dt)^3] + \omega_0^2 v = (E/\omega_1) \sin \omega_1 t \qquad (4.2.2)$$

Let us assume that $v(t)$ has the form

$$v(t) = b_1(t) \sin \omega_1 t + b_2(t) \cos \omega_1 t \qquad (4.2.3)$$

where b_1 and b_2 are slowly varing functions of time; i.e.,

$$db_1/dt = \delta B_1(b_1, b_2), \qquad db_2/dt = \delta B_2(b_1, b_2) \qquad (4.2.4)$$

where δ is a small number.

This assumption is justified if we are close to entrainment.

Equation (4.2.3) can now be put into Eq. (4.2.2). If one ignores all the terms which are multiplied either by higher powers of ε and δ or by their products (i.e., ε^2, δ^2, $\varepsilon\delta$, $\varepsilon^2\delta$,..., etc.), then the result is simplified considerably. By equating the coefficients of the $\sin \omega_1 t$ and $\cos \omega_1 t$ terms we obtain

$$2\omega_1 \frac{db_2}{dt} - (\omega_0^2 - \omega_1^2)\,b_1 - \varepsilon\omega_1 b_2 \left[1 - \frac{\omega_1^2}{4}(b_1^2 + b_2^2)\right] = -\frac{E}{\omega_1} \qquad (4.2.5)$$

and

$$2\omega_1 \frac{db_1}{dt} + (\omega_0{}^2 - \omega_1{}^2)\, b_2 - \varepsilon\omega_1 b_1 \left[1 - \frac{\omega_1{}^2}{4}(b_1{}^2 + b_2{}^2)\right] = 0 \qquad (4.2.6)$$

These equations can be further simplified by using the following substitutions:

$$X = b_1\omega_1/2, \qquad Y = b_2\omega_1/2, \qquad R^2 = X^2 + Y^2$$

$$\tau = \varepsilon t/2, \qquad h = (\omega_0{}^2 - \omega_1{}^2)/\varepsilon\omega_1\,, \qquad A = -E/2\varepsilon\omega_1 \qquad (4.2.7)$$

The result is

$$dX/d\tau = X(1 - R^2) - hY \qquad (4.2.8)$$

$$dY/d\tau = Y(1 - R^2) + hX + A \qquad (4.2.9)$$

X and Y are simply normalized amplitudes of the oscillation, h corresponds to the difference of the natural frequency of the oscillator and the external frequency, while A corresponds to the amplitude of the external input.

If entrainment occurs, only the frequency ω_1 should be observed in the output of the oscillator and therefore X and Y (or b_1 and b_2) should be constant. If the entrainment is stable, then any variations in X and Y should damp out. Therefore the van der Pol oscillator of Eq. (4.2.1) will be entrained by the input $E \cos \omega_1 t$ if the system of Eqs. (4.2.8) and (4.2.9) has a singularity. The entrainment will be stable if that singularity is stable.

This is a considerable simplification and the validity of its result is limited by the extent to which the assumptions of small ε and δ hold. The method is of course applicable to any other oscillators, besides the one of van der Pol, which satisfy these assumptions.

The coordinates of the singularity of the system of Eqs. (4.2.8) and (4.2.9) are given by

$$X_0 = -h\rho/A \qquad (4.2.10)$$

$$Y_0 = -(1 - \rho)\rho/A \qquad (4.2.11)$$

$$\rho = X_0{}^2 + Y_0{}^2 \qquad (4.2.12)$$

provided that ρ satisfies the following equation:

$$\rho[(1 - \rho)^2 + h^2] = A^2 \qquad (4.2.13)$$

The latter is the important equation of our study. Quite often we are less interested in the relative phase of the oscillation with respect to the external input than in the amplitude of that oscillation and the possibility of the occurrence of entrainment. If Eq. (4.2.13) has a positive real solution with respect to ρ, then entrainment is possible (although it might not be stable). If no such solutions exist entrainment is not possible.

Because of the difficulties involved in solving cubic equations, Eq. (4.2.13) is often plotted as a relation between ρ and h for a given A and then solved graphically. Figure 4.2.1 shows two such curves. For small

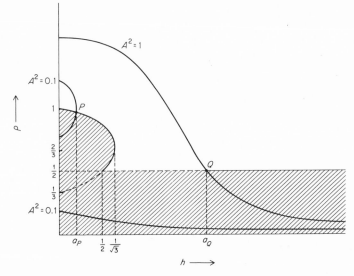

Fig. 4.2.1. Graphical illustration of the relation between entraining amplitude (represented by A) difference in frequencies (represented by h) and normalized amplitude of the oscillation ρ. No stable entrainment can occur within the shaded area.

A there are three positive real roots while for large A there is only one.

We turn now to the question of stability. To this goal we replace X and Y in Eqs. (4.2.8) and (4.2.9) by $X_0 + \xi$ and $Y_0 + \eta$, we obtain the linearized equations for ξ and η (ignoring quadratic terms), and then calculate the characteristic polynomial for this linear system. It turns out to be

$$\lambda^2 + 2(2\rho - 1)\lambda + [(1 - \rho)(1 - 3\rho) + h^2] = 0 \qquad (4.2.14)$$

For stability it is necessary and sufficient that both coefficients are positive; i.e.,

$$\rho > \tfrac{1}{2} \qquad (4.2.15)$$

$$(1 - \rho)(1 - 3\rho) + h^2 > 0 \qquad (4.2.16)$$

The last equation represents the region outside an ellipse with center at

$$\rho = \tfrac{2}{3}, \qquad h = 0$$

and lengths of the h axis equal to $1/\sqrt{3}$ and the ρ axis equal to $\tfrac{1}{3}$. Note also that for $\rho = \tfrac{1}{2}$ the ellipse passes through $h = \tfrac{1}{2}$.

These regions are also indicated on Fig. 4.2.1 and they determine the *limits of entrainment*.

Thus for a large amplitude the point Q determines the value a_Q above which there can be no stable entrainment. For a small amplitude the corresponding points are P and a_P. Recall that h as given by Eq. (4.2.7) corresponds to the normalized frequency difference.

Figure 4.2.1 with Eqs. (4.2.7) allows us to study the effect of various parameters. In particular it can be seen that both ω_1 and ε affect in the same manner h and A. Equation (4.2.13) gives for $\rho = \tfrac{1}{2}$ the coordinates of the point Q:

$$h_Q{}^2 = 2A^2 - \tfrac{1}{4}$$

or, using Eqs. (4.2.7),

$$4(\omega_0{}^2 - \omega_1{}^2)^2 = 2E^2 - \varepsilon^2\omega_1{}^2 \tag{4.2.17}$$

For a given E and ω_1 the difference $\omega_0{}^2 - \omega_1{}^2$ is a decreasing function of ε. In other words, entrainment is easier for weakly nonlinear oscillators. This result is misleading because it has been derived on the basis of the assumption that ε is very small. Actually the opposite is true because of the fact that the actual limit of entrainment is less than the theoretical for large values of ε. We will return to this point in a little while.

In order to find the coordinates of the point P we must solve simultaneously Eqs. (4.2.13) and (4.2.16) (set equal to zero). Subtracting one from the other we obtain

$$2\rho^2(1 - \rho) = A^2 \tag{4.2.18}$$

The value of ρ so obtained can be placed back into Eq. (4.2.16) to give the value of a_P. Because for small A the value of ρ should be close to one, we may attempt an approximate solution by replacing the term $1 - \rho$ from Eq. (4.2.18) into Eq. (4.2.16) while setting $\rho = 1$ everywhere else. Then we obtain

$$h^2 \cong A^2 \tag{4.2.19}$$

and, in this case, the effect of ε on the limits of entrainment is much smaller than before.

The relative phase between the oscillation and the input can be determined as follows:

Equation (4.2.3) can be written as

$$v(t) = (b_1{}^2 + b_2{}^2)^{1/2} \sin(\omega_1 t + \phi) \qquad (4.2.20)$$

where

$$\tan \phi = b_2(t)/b_1(t) \qquad (4.2.21)$$

Using the values of the normalized variables at the singularity the above equations become

$$v(t) = (2/\omega_1) \sqrt{\rho} \sin(\omega_1 t + \phi) \qquad (4.2.22)$$

and

$$\tan \phi = Y_0/X_0 = (1 - \rho)/h \qquad (4.2.23)$$

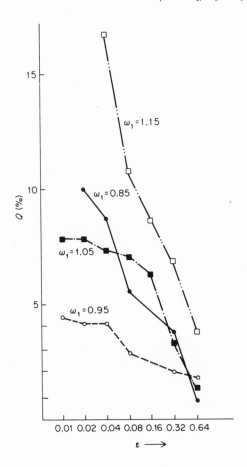

FIG. 4.2.2.   Plot of the quality of entrainment (represented by Q) versus the degree of nonlinearity (represented by ε). Theoretical entrainment corresponds to $Q = 0$. Each one of four lines denotes a different value of ω_1 ($\omega_0 = 1$ in all cases).

or, for the original variable $x(t)$ in Eq. (4.2.1),

$$x(t) = 2 \sqrt{\rho} \cos(\omega_1 t + \phi) \tag{4.2.24}$$

while

$$\tan \phi = \frac{1 - \rho}{\omega_0^2 - \omega_1^2} \varepsilon \omega_1 \tag{4.2.25}$$

If the amplitude E is close to the limit of entrainment, then ρ is less than 1 and the sign of the tangent is that of $\omega_0^2 - \omega_1^2$. However the opposite is true if ρ exceeds 1. The latter is often the case in practice. Then if the external stimulus has a frequency higher than ω_0, $x(t)$ leads the input. If the external frequency is lower than ω_0, then $x(t)$ lags behind the input.

The dependence of the sign of the phase difference on the amplitude of the oscillation makes it also dependent on the strength of the stimulus and on ε, as one can see from Eq. (4.2.13). Therefore blanket statements

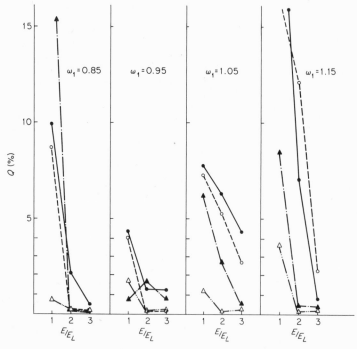

FIG. 4.2.3. Plot of the quality of entrainment versus the normalized entraining amplitude E/E_L for each one of four values of ω_1. Four values of ε were tested: (——) 0.01, (---) 0.04, (–·–) 0.16, (–··–) 0.64.

about phase relations during entrainment are not valid. Arguments based on intuition give the correct answer only part of the time. (Compare also Sections 4.3 and 4.5.)

Figures 4.2.2–4.2.4 illustrate the results of computer simulations. The following measure of entrainment is used. A period T_x is calculated from successive crossings of $x(t)$ and a period $T_{\dot{x}}$ similarly from $\dot{x}(t)$. For each one its percent difference from $2\pi/\omega_1$ is computed and the sum Q of those two quantities is used as a measure. Values less than 0.5% correspond to fairly good entrainment while values over 10% definitely denote lack of entrainment. In a series of tests illustrated in Fig. 4.2.2 the value of E was taken from Eq. (4.2.17). It is seen that Q is a logarithmically decreasing function of ε. Entrainment is poor in all cases for $\varepsilon \leqslant 0.16$. However, for $\varepsilon = 0.64$, Q is between 1 and 2% except for $\omega_1 = 1.15$. Figure 4.2.3 shows Q as a function of E/E_L, where E_L is the value of E obtained from Eq. (4.2.17). Entrainment is poor for $\varepsilon = 0.01$ throughout, but it is fairly good for $\varepsilon \geqslant 0.04$ and E/E_L over 2.

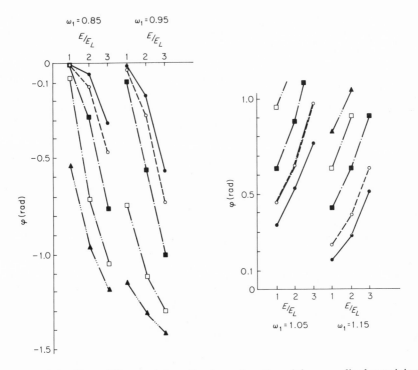

FIG. 4.2.4. Phase difference ϕ (in radians) as a function of the normalized entraining amplitude E/E_L for each one of four values of ω_1. Five values of ε were tested: (——) 0.01, (---) 0.02, (–·–) 0.08, (–···–) 0.32, (–····–) 0.64.

Figure 4.2.4 shows the dependence of the phase angle ϕ on the frequency ω_1 and the relative amplitude E/E_L. (Since E_L varies little over most of the range of ε the abscissa is also proportional to E.) It is seen that the absolute value of ϕ is an increasing function of "strength" of the input. This is expected from Eq. (4.2.25) which was used to plot these curves from values of ρ obtained by computer simulation (ρ is obviously an increasing function of E). In some cases the values of ϕ measured directly from the zero crossings of $x(t)$ were compared and good agreement was found, especially for the smaller values of ε.

In concluding this section we must again emphasize that, although this analysis was carried out on a van der Pol oscillator, its qualitative results are valid for all weakly nonlinear oscillators.

4.3 Entrainment of Circadian Clocks by Light and Temperature Cycles

There is a wealth of data on entrainment of circadian rhythms by light and temperature cycles [Bru-2, Bün-A]. It is probably the most common type of experiment performed by researchers in the field. In the early days the results of such work helped establish the endogenous nature of the biological clock. It is well beyond the scope of this treatise to give a comprehensive survey of all experiments of this kind. From an analytical viewpoint many have rather simple results. Entrainment is obtained to cycles of light and temperature variations with periods close to 24 hours. Also the phase of the rhythm can be modified by cycles of exactly 24 hours but with different times of illumination than the natural day-night sequence. If one assumes that the rhythm is governed by an endogenous self-sustained nonlinear oscillator, then these results are not surprising.

We will present here a summary of results which illustrate the quantitative aspects of entrainment and in particular the dependence of the limits of entrainment on the amplitude of the input.

The latter relation is of more than "academic" importance for animals living in the arctic where the changes in illumination over 24 hours are quite small. A set of illustrative experiments have been reported by Swade and Pittendrigh [Swa-2]. The animals were exposed to a smoothly varying light intensity of a 24-hour cycle. Entrainment in this case means "locking" of the phase of activity to the input as well as to a period of 24 hours. (Let us not forget that the free running period is in general different than 24 hours.) Figure 4.3.1 shows the form of the stimulus which consisted of a sinusoidal variation with a chopped

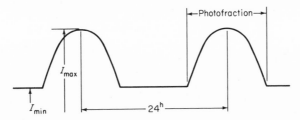

FIG. 4.3.1. Light variation over a 24-hour cycle in order to test entrainment of animals to weak stimuli [Swa-1].

minimum. The term *photofraction* refers to the part of the period where the light intensity is above the minimum. Four nocturnal and three diurnal species of rodents were studied involving a total of about 30 individual animals. It turned out that the important parameters controlling entrainment were the ratio of the maximum intensity I_{max} over the minimum intensity I_{min} and the length of the photofraction rather than the average level of illumination. This is not surprising in view of the adaptive properties of the visual system.

Tables 4.3.1 and 4.3.2 summarize the results in terms of percentages of experiments where entrainment occurred. When entrainment failed two kinds of behavior were observed: either oscillatory free runs or loss of any rhythmic output. We will discuss these aspects in the next section. The contents of the tables are illustrated in Fig. 4.3.2. It is seen clearly that above a certain threshold value entrainment is much more likely to occur. Entrainment tends to fail for values of the ratios I_{max}/I_{min} less than 5.

Hoffman [Hof-4, Hof-6] has conducted a similar study using 24-hour sinosoidal temperature cycles to entrain the locomotor activity of lizards

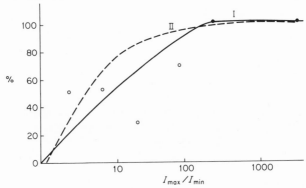

FIG. 4.3.2. Percent of animals entrained for various ratios of maximum over minimum light intensity [Swa-1].

TABLE 4.3.1[a]

I_{max}/I_{min}	Entrainment (%)	Oscillatory free run (%)	Arrythmic behavior (%)
I. Nocturnal species—photofraction > 20 hours (77)[b]			
>1000	100	0	0
380	100	0	0
52	75	13	12
2–5	30	43	27
II. Nocturnal species—photofraction 7–12 hours (50)[b]			
670, 760	88	0	12
31	100	0	0
10–12	79	11	10
6–8	67	8	25
4	25	0	75
2	0	0	100
III. Diurnal species—photofraction > 17 hours (43)[b]			
>359	75	0	25
15–27	27	0	73
7–18	46	0	54
2–6	53	0	47
IV. Diurnal species—photofraction 8–12 hours (28)[b]			
>1000	100	0	0
23	100	0	0
8–10	10	20	70
2–5	45	0	55

[a] (Adapted from Swade and Pittendrigh [Swa-1].)
[b] Number of experiments performed.

(of the species *Lacerta sicula*). The following is a summary of his results: A number of animals (about 15), were exposed to temperature variations of different amplitudes under constant-light environment. The percentage of animals reaching synchrony decreased with a decrease in the amplitude of the variation. Table 4.3.2 shows this dependence.

These results bear strong similarity to those of the previous table. However the data can give additional information if one looks at the free-running period of the various individual animals. Those with periods between 23.5 and 24.5 either were entrained or showed tendency for entrainment for all variations (with two exceptions for 0.9°C). On the other hand, an animal with free-running period of 23 hours entrained only for the largest variation (7.2°C).

TABLE 4.3.2ᵃ

ENTRAINMENT OF A CIRCADIAN RHYTHM BY TEMPERATURE CYCLES

Temperature variation (°C) (range)	Definite entrainment (%)	Probable entrainment (%)	Definite oscillatory free run (%)	Probable oscillatory free run (%)	No discernible influence of the input (%)
7.2 (19.2–26.9)	95	—	—	5	0
3.6 (18.5–22.1)	75	13	12	0	0
1.6 (19.4–21)	75	13	12	0	0
0.9 (18.8–19.7)	33	33	7	7	20

ᵃ (Adapted from Hoffmann [Hof-6]).

Recently Feldman [Fel-4] has reported similar results in *Neurospora crassa* where mutants with short free running periods (e.q. 16.5 hours) show lower upper limits of entrainment.

Hoffman also describes the relations between phase phase difference, period, and temperature variation. Figure 4.3.3 summarizes these

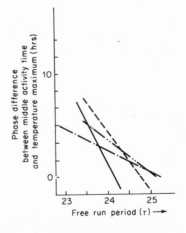

FIG. 4.3.3. Phase shift ϕ as a function of the endogenous period τ. In all cases the entraining frequency was 24 hours. Four amplitudes of temperature cycles were used [Hof-6]: (——) 0.9°C, (---) 1.6°C, (–·–) 3.6°C, (–··–) 7.2°C.

results. The phase is measured in hours between the middle of the period when an animal is active and the maximum of the temperature cycle. Positive numbers denoted that the former leads the latter. The abscissa is the free-running period, τ. If the phase for individual animals with τ equal to 24 hours is taken as a basis, then one can talk about a relative phase advance when τ is less than 24 and a relative phase delay when τ exceeds 24. In terms of Eq. (4.2.25), we have an agreement between the sign of ϕ and the sign of $\omega_0{}^2 - \omega_1{}^2$. The dependence is steeper for small variations than for large.

4.4   Fringe Entrainment

The behavior of a nonlinear oscillator with characteristic frequency ω_0 subject to a periodic input with frequency ω_1 outside the range of entrainment (or subharmonic entrainment) is generally very complex. In general one observes components with both frequencies ω_0 and ω_1. However, because of the nonlinear nature of the system, there is no simple superposition.

A more interesting case occurs if ω_1 is close to the limits of entrainment for a given amplitude of the input. Then one observes beats at a frequency equal to $| \omega_0 - \omega_1 |$. This can be shown easily in the following way.

Let T_0 be the average period of the oscillator under perturbation by the external input and let T_1 be the period of the latter. After each cycle there will be an average phase shift equal to

$$T_0 - T_1$$

If after, say, k cycles of the oscillator the accumulated phase difference equals the period of the input, the relative phases will be the same as in the beginning of the count and the phenomena associated with the interaction of the two oscillations will repeat themselves. Therefore the value of k should be given by

$$k \, | \, T_1 - T_0 \, | = T_1 \qquad (4.4.1)$$

and the time T required for the repetition will be kT_0 or

$$T = T_1 T_0 / | \, T_1 - T_0 \, | \qquad (4.4.2)$$

This is equivalent to

$$1/T = | \, 1/T_1 - 1/T_0 \, | \qquad \text{or} \qquad \omega = | \, \omega_1 - \omega_0 \, | \qquad (4.4.3)$$

Note that the common derivation of the frequency of the beats on the basis of a trigonometric identity is not justified here because the law of superposition does not hold for a nonlinear system.

Such beats have been observed experimentally by Swade and Pittendrigh [Swa-2] and by Hoffman [Hof-4, Hof-6] and have been described as *oscillatory free runs*. Tables 4.3.1 and 4.3.2 indicate their

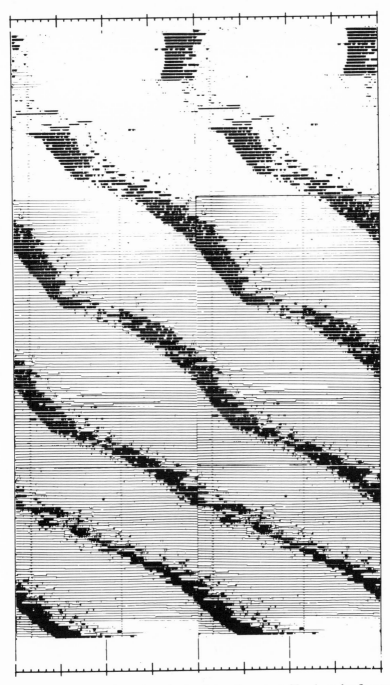

Fig. 4.4.1. Records of running-wheel activity of a rodent. Top is under fluctuating light between 59 and 13 f-c. The rest of the records are under fluctuating light between 38 and 18 f-c [Swa-1, Fig. 79].

incidence near the limits of entrainment. A periodic fluctuation in the length of the period is not in itself sufficient indication for the occurrence of beats described above. A quantitative test would be the check of the previous observation; namely, that over a period of the fluctuation the total phase shifts equals approximately T_0. Figure 4.4.1 shows an experimental record [Swa-1] where this observation holds for a rodent. The period of the beats there is about 42 days.

Hoffman's data, on the other hand, do not allow this verification. The length of the oscillatory free runs, he reports, does not exceed 30 days, and this is a rather short interval of observation for this type of phenomena.

This explanation of oscillatory free runs was first proposed by Pavlidis [Pav-7]. It is the simplest but not the only explanation described in the literature [Swa-3].

Mixtures of frequencies and beats have also been observed by other investigators, not only in circadian rhythms [Lam-1] but also in biochemical oscillations [Pye-1].

4.5   Entrainment of Oscillators by Pulses

In many cases of biological interest the entrainment of oscillators is performed by discrete stimuli, usually in the form of pulses. Then the analysis of Section 4.2 is not directly applicable, while under certain conditions the use of the phase response curves is more helpful.

Indeed suppose that an oscillator with free-run period equal to T is exposed to a sequence of stimuli S, occurring every T_1 units of time. Furthermore assume that not only the duration of S is less than T_1 but also that during that time the state of the system returns close enough to the limit cycle to justify the use of the PRC for the next occurrence of S (see Section 3.4).

Then the following analysis is applicable. Equation (3.4.1) can be used to express the phase q_n of the system right after the application of the nth stimulus in terms of the phase p_n, just before the application of that stimulus:

$$q_n = \{p_n + f(p_n)\}_{\text{mod}\,T} \tag{4.5.1}$$

The phase p_{n+1} just before the application of the $(n + 1)$th stimulus will be given by

$$p_{n+1} = \{q_n + T_1\}_{\text{mod}\,T} \tag{4.5.2}$$

or

$$p_{n+1} = \{p_n + f(p_n) + T_1\}_{\text{mod}\,T} \tag{4.5.3}$$

Obviously a necessary condition for entrainment is that

$$p_{n+1} = p_n \tag{4.5.4}$$

This may happen in either one of the following two ways:

$$f(p_n) + T_1 = 0 \tag{4.5.5}$$

$$f(p_n) + T_1 = kT, \quad k \text{ an integer} \tag{4.5.6}$$

The first case corresponds to a resetting of the oscillation rather than entrainment, and it is of no further interest in the present discussion.

The second case corresponds to harmonic entrainment if $k = 1$ or to superharmonic entrainment if $k > 1$. In the latter case k "cycles" of the system correspond to one "cycle" of S.

Let A be the maximum phase advance of the PRC for S and let D be the maximum phase delay for the same conditions. In terms of the notation of the previous chapter we have

$$A = \max_p f(p) \tag{4.5.7}$$

$$D = |\min_p f(p)| \tag{4.5.8}$$

Let also p_A and p_D denote the locations where these extrema occur (not necessarily unique).

Then Eq. (4.5.6) may be solved with respect to T_1 to give the maximum and minimum values for entrainment:

$$T_{1\,\text{max}} = kT + D \tag{4.5.9}$$

$$T_{1\,\text{min}} = kT - A \tag{4.5.10}$$

Thus the *range of harmonic entrainment* is given by

$$T - A \leqslant T_1 \leqslant T + D \tag{4.5.11}$$

and, in general, the range for superharmonic entrainment by

$$kT - A \leqslant T_1 \leqslant kT + D \tag{4.5.12}$$

The above inequalities give necessary but not sufficient conditions. We must obviously require that the entrainment be *stable*, i.e., that the difference equation (4.5.3) have a stable solution

$$p_{n+1} = p_n \equiv p^*$$

A well-known result from the theory of difference equations [Jur-I, Lev-I] is that, if the derivative of the right-hand side computed at the solution is less than 1 in absolute value, then the solution is stable. In the present case this requires that

$$\left| \frac{d\{p + f(p) + T_1\}_{\bmod T}}{dp} \right| < 1 \quad \text{at} \quad p = p^*$$

or

$$|\, 1 + df(p)/dp \,| < 1 \quad \text{at} \quad p = p^* \tag{4.5.13}$$

The last equation is equivalent to

$$-2 < df(p)/dp < 0 \quad \text{at} \quad p = p^* \tag{4.5.14}$$

This constraint makes it necessary to modify the limits of entrainment by defining A and D as the maximum phase shifts only over the region of the PRC where Eq. (4.5.14) is satisfied; namely,

$$A' = \max_{p \in R} f(p), \qquad R = \text{interval where } -2 < f'(p) < 0 \tag{4.5.15}$$

$$D' = |\min_{p \in R} f(p)|, \qquad R = \text{interval where } -2 < f'(p) < 0 \tag{4.5.16}$$

Then the range of *stable entrainment* will be given by

$$kT - A' \leqslant T_1 \leqslant kT + D', \quad k \geqslant 1 \tag{4.5.17}$$

We will now use this methodology to study the case when two occurrences of S during a period are noted.

Let the sequence of stimuli consist of pairs T_1 time units apart followed by pairs T_2 time units apart, as shown in Fig. 4.5.1. Thus the period of that sequence is

$$T_S = T_1 + T_2 \tag{4.5.18}$$

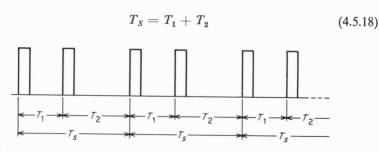

FIG. 4.5.1.   A sequence of pairs of pulses.

Let p_n be the phase just before the nth pulse which is followed by a pulse after T_1 units of time. Then, as before,

$$p_{n+1} = \{p_n + f(p_n) + T_1\}_{\text{mod}\,T} \tag{4.5.3'}$$

The phase right after this pulse will be

$$q_{n+1} = \{p_{n+1} + f(p_{n+1})\}_{\text{mod}\,T} \tag{4.5.19}$$

and the phase just before the next pulse

$$p_{n+2} = \{p_{n+1} + f(p_{n+1}) + T_2\}_{\text{mod}\,T} \tag{4.5.20}$$

Entrainment now requires that

$$p_{n+2} = p_n \tag{4.5.21}$$

This may happen in either one of the following two ways:

$$f(p_n) + f(p_{n+1}) + T_S = 0 \tag{4.5.22}$$

$$f(p_n) + f(p_{n+1}) + T_S = kT, \quad k \text{ an integer} \tag{4.5.23}$$

Again the first case corresponds to resetting of the oscillation and it is not of any further interest.

The second case can give the limits of entrainment as follows:
Let

$$B = \max_p [f(p) + f(p + f(p) + T_1)] \tag{4.5.24}$$

and

$$E = |\min_p [f(p) + f(p + f(p) + T_1)]| \tag{4.5.25}$$

Then the range will be given by

$$kT - B \leqslant T_S \leqslant kT + E \tag{4.5.26}$$

Because of the repeated application of Eq. (4.5.3) it is not possible to repeat the stability analysis in as concise a way as before. The differentiation of the right-hand side of Eq. (4.5.20) after substitution of Eq. (4.5.3') yields the condition

$$|[1 + f'(p_n)][1 + f'(p_{n+1})]| < 1 \tag{4.5.27}$$

or

$$-2 < f'(p_n) + f'(p_{n+1}) + f'(p_n) f'(p_{n+1}) < 0 \tag{4.5.28}$$

In certain cases one pulse may fall into the flat region of a PRC; i.e.,

$$f(p_{n+1}) = 0 \qquad (4.5.29)$$

and

$$f'(p_{n+1}) = 0 \qquad (4.5.30)$$

Then it is true that

$$B = A, \qquad E = D$$

and the situation is similar to entrainment by a train of pulses every T_S units.

Also, using the same assumptions as in Section 3.4, we may consider entrainment by a stimulus of duration T_1 followed by another occurring T_2 time units after the end of the previous one, and so forth. For values of T_1 short in comparison to the duration of the insensitive zone, the situation will not be any different than the one before. If T_1 is a little longer, then the effect will be the same as of a short duration S followed by a second one after T_1 units. In all these cases the effect of a "continuous" stimulus of duration T_1 will be the same as the effect of two "short" ones occurring at the beginning and the end of its duration.

If T_1 is even longer, then it will have the effect of S leaving always the system at a particular phase q^* (the end of the insensitive zone) no matter when S started. Actually the phase at the start will reach quickly the value

$$p_n = \{q^* + T_2\}_{\mathrm{mod}\,T} \qquad (4.5.31)$$

Let T^* be the minimum time required for the system to reach from q^* the state triggering the timing event. Then if

$$T_2 > T^* \qquad (4.5.32)$$

we will have stable entrainment. Otherwise the oscillation will be effectively damped.

The above development is primarily due to the work of Pittendrigh [Pit-5, Pit-6, Pit-7] and some of its details to that of Ottesen [Ott-1] and Pavlidis [Pav-3].

4.6   Entrainment of a Circadian Rhythm by Light Pulses

The analysis of the previous sections has been found to be directly applicable in the study of the eclosion rhythm of the fruitfly *Drosophila pseudoobscura*. (As a matter of fact, experimentation and analysis proceeded together.) Figure 3.2.2 shows a PRC for 15-min light pulses for this rhythm. It can be readily seen that for this curve the quantities A' and D' [defined by Eqs. (4.5.15) and (4.5.16)] equal

$$A' = 5.9 \text{ hours}, \qquad D' = 5.6 \text{ hours}$$

Therefore the limits of entrainment should be approximately between 18 and 30 hours. This has been indeed verified experimentally. A more interesting set of experiments involves the use of a pair of short pulses or one long pulse of light followed by a period of darkness.

In this case q^* equals 12 hours. The sudden transitions from delays into advances occurs around 18 hours and, in terms of the models of Section 3.4, this would imply that this is when the timing event is triggered. Thus the quantity T^* defined in the previous section should

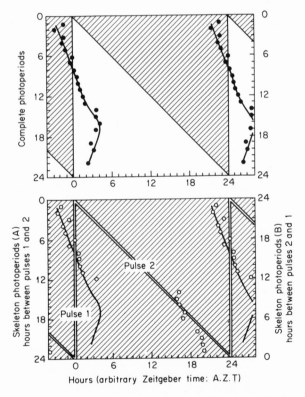

FIG. 4.6.1.   The phase of the *Drosophila pseudoobscura* eclosion rhythm as a function of complete (upper panel) and skeleton (lower panel) photoperiods. The plotted points are medians of the steady-state distributions of eclosion. In the lower panel the solid curve is that fitted to the medians for complete photoperiods in the upper panel [Pit-5].

equal about 6 hours and entrainment should be possible as long as the duration of the dark period exceeded that length. It turns out that entrainment is possible for even shorter dark periods. This is demonstrated in Fig. 4.6.1 describing experimental results obtained by Pittendrigh and Minis [Pit-5]. In addition to entrainment by full photo periods this figure also describes entrainment by *skeleton* photoperiods; namely, by pairs of short pulses occurring at the same time as the beginning and the end of the full photoperiods. It is seen that for T_1 up to about 12 hours the pair of short pulses imitates completely a pulse of duration T_1. However for T_1 greater than 12 hours the skeleton photoperiod behaves in about the same way as a full photoperiod of duration T_2. This kind of behavior is similar to the one discussed in the previous section where, for T_1 comparable in length to the flat zone of the PRC, one could not distinguish between a pulse of length T_1 and two short pulses T_1 time units apart. However for greater values of T_1 the two responses should be qualitatively different, which indeed is the case with Fig. 4.6.1. The differences for large T_1 eliminate an alternative hypothesis: that the organism perceives light only through ON–OFF

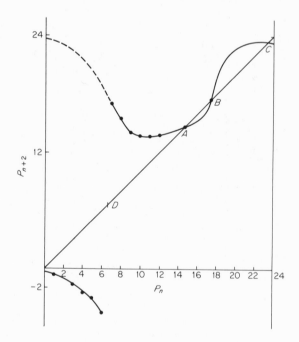

FIG. 4.6.2. Plot of P_{n+2} vs P_n for an entraining environment of $T_1 = T_2 = 12$ hours (according to the notation of Fig. 4.5.1).

receptors. If this were true the simulation of continuous photoperiods by skeleton photoperiods would not depend on T_1.

Probably the most striking result of such experiments occurs for values of T_1 between 10 and 14 hours. For them it is possible to have two different types of entrainment. This can also be explained in terms of the analysis of the previous section. A substitution of Eq. (4.5.3') into (4.5.20) gives

$$p_{n+2} = \{p_n + f(p_n) + f[(p_n + f(p_n) + T_1)_{\mathrm{mod}T}]\}_{\mathrm{mod}T} \qquad (4.6.1)$$

Using the data from the PRC of Fig. 3.2.2 for $T_1 = 12$ hours and $T_2 = 12$ hours we obtain the curve of Fig. 4.6.2. It can be readily seen that this is intersected by the line with unit slope at 3 points: A, 14.5 hours (with slope close to zero); B, 18.5 hours (with slope much greater than one); and C, 23.5 hours (with slope close to zero). From Fig. 3.2.2 one can see that the phase shifts at 14.5 and 23.5 are of opposite sign; thus, Eq. (4.5.23) is satisfied for $k = 1$ (since $T_S = T$ in the present case). The phase shift at 18.5 is close to 12; thus, this point may be

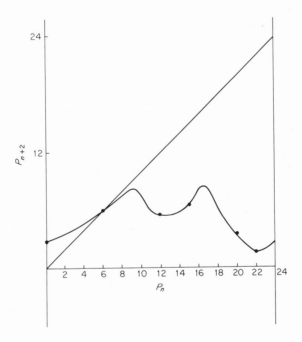

Fig. 4.6.3. Plot of P_{n+2} vs P_n for an entraining environment of $T_1 = 4$, $T_2 = 20$ (according to the notation of Fig. 4.5.1).

interpreted as being advanced by 12 hours and the system returning at the same state for the second pulse; i.e., it is a case with

$$p_n = p_{n+1} \tag{4.6.2}$$

and

$$f(p_n) \cong T/2 \tag{4.6.3}$$

In terms of Eq. (4.5.23) we have $k = 2$. The interpretation of these data is that we have two possible states of entrainment; B corresponds to an unstable state. If the first pulse in a free-running system is applied at time less than 18.5 but greater than 6.5 (point D), then the system will reach the steady state A, while it will reach C if the first pulse is outside that interval. In a sense, the discontinuity point D can be considered as an unstable equilibrium point.

Figure 4.6.3 shows the relation between p_{n+2} and p_n for $T_1 = 4$ and $T_2 = 20$. It is then seen that there is a unique (and stable) solution of Eq. (4.6.1).

This section follows closely the work of Pittendrigh and his co-workers [Pit-5, Pit-6, Pit-7, Ott-1]. For more details on the experimental results the reader can consult the original references. Edmunds [Edm-5] has also studied entrainment by skeleton photoperiods in *Euglena*.

4.7 Subharmonic Entrainment

If the characteristic frequency of the oscillator is close to an integer submultiple of the frequency of the input, it is possible to have entrainment to that submultiple. This phenomenon is called subharmonic entrainment or frequency demultiplication [But-I, Haa-I, Hay-I, Min-I, San-I].

We will describe it first for the case when the input is a sequence of short-duration pulses by using the methods of Section 4.5. If T_1 is the time between two successive pulses, we have the following relation for the phase p_{n+1} at the time of the application of the $(n + 1)$th pulse in terms of p_n [same as Eq. (4.5.3)]:

$$p_{n+1} = \{p_n + f(p_n) + T_1\}_{\mathrm{mod}\,T} \tag{4.7.1}$$

Entrainment to the mth subharmonic will occur if

$$p_{n+m} = p_n + \sum_{i=n}^{n+m-1} f(p_i) + mT_1 = p_n + T \tag{4.7.2}$$

or if

$$\sum_{i=n}^{n+m-1} f(p_i) + mT_1 = T \qquad (4.7.3)$$

If mT_1 equals exactly T, then the sum of phase shifts should be zero. A cursory look at the PRC's shown in Chapter 3 reveals that this is not a difficult condition to satisfy in the case of circadian rhythms. During a large part of the daily cycle $f(p)$ equals zero and the rest is divided about equally between positive and negative values.

The entrainment will obviously be stable if

$$\left| \prod_{i=1}^{m} (1 + f'(p_i)) \right| < 1 \qquad (4.7.4)$$

If mT_1 is not equal to T, then the sum of the phase shifts should equal their difference. The limits of entrainment in this case can be determined in the same manner as before.

It should be emphasized that it is possible to have periods where entrainment of any order fail. This can happen if the limits of entrainment around each subharmonic do not overlap. Thus a situation as shown in Fig. 4.7.1 can be expected.

The case of subharmonic entrainment of weakly nonlinear oscillators

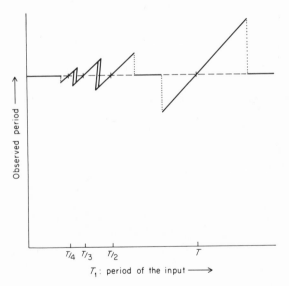

FIG. 4.7.1. The regions with slope zero denote lack of entrainment.

has been treated extensively in the mathematical literature [But-I, Haa-I, Min-I]. In particular let us consider the following system:

$$d^2x/dt^2 + x = \mu f(x, dx/dt) + E \sin \omega t \qquad (4.7.5)$$

where ω is an integer. The characteristic frequency of the autonomous system is assumed equal to one. Subharmonic entrainment will occur if the nonautonomous system has a solution with period equal to one. The analysis of the system is facilitated if one introduces a transformation

$$z = x - \frac{E}{1 - \omega^2} \sin \omega t \qquad (4.7.6)$$

and then

$$u = (dz/dt) \cos t + z \sin t \qquad (4.7.7)$$

$$v = (dz/dt) \sin t - z \cos t \qquad (4.7.8)$$

The original equation is transformed into

$$du/dt = \mu\psi(u, v, t) \cos t \qquad (4.7.9a)$$

$$dv/dt = \mu\psi(u, v, t) \sin t \qquad (4.7.9b)$$

where

$$\psi(u, v, t) = f\left(u \sin t - v \cos t + \frac{E}{1 - \omega^2} \sin \omega t,\right.$$

$$\left. u \cos t + v \sin t + \frac{\omega E}{1 - \omega^2} \cos \omega t\right) \qquad (4.7.10)$$

One can now assume in a similar manner as in Section 4.2 that the solution of Eq. (4.4.6) is of the form

$$x(t) = u(\mu, t) \sin t - v(\mu, t) \cos t + \frac{E}{1 - \omega^2} \sin \omega t \qquad (4.7.11)$$

One can then determine the form of u and v by asymptotic techniques. In particular it can be shown that a necessary condition for u and v to be periodic with period 1 is that there exist constants a, b such that

$$\int_0^{2\pi} \psi(a, b, t) \cos t \, dt = 0 \qquad (4.7.12a)$$

and

$$\int_0^{2\pi} \psi(a, b, t) \sin t \, dt = 0 \qquad (4.7.12b)$$

An additional condition is

$$\left\{ \int_0^{2\pi} \left[\frac{\partial \psi}{\partial u} \right] \cos t \, dt \right\} \left\{ \int_0^{2\pi} \left[\frac{\partial \psi}{\partial v} \right] \sin t \, dt \right\}$$

$$- \left\{ \int_0^{2\pi} \left[\frac{\partial \psi}{\partial u} \right] \sin t \, dt \right\} \left\{ \int_0^{2\pi} \left[\frac{\partial \psi}{\partial v} \right] \cos t \, dt \right\} \neq 0 \qquad (4.7.13)$$

where the partial derivatives of ψ are calculated for the values a and b found from Eqs. (4.7.12) [Min-I].

The above conditions are also sufficient for the existence of subharmonic entrainment, but they do not guarantee its stability. The analysis for the latter is quite involved and it is outside the scope of this monograph.

In general the establishment of subharmonic entrainment depends not only on the values of E and ω but also on the initial conditions of the oscillator.

Hayashi [Hay-I] has studied extensively these questions, especially for oscillators with linear damping and nonlinear restoring terms of the form

$$d^2x/dt^2 + 2\mu \, dx/dt + g(x) = E \sin \omega t \qquad (4.7.14)$$

It turns out that the order of subharmonic oscillations which can be established depends strongly on the form of $g(x)$. For example, if

$$g(x) = c_1 x + c_3 x^3 \qquad (4.7.15)$$

only a third-order subharmonic is possible. For

$$g(x) = c_1 x + c_5 x^5 \qquad (4.7.16)$$

both third- and fifth-order subharmonics are possible.

A partial explanation for these results can be seen by using linearization techniques (of the form used in Section 4.2) in studying Eq. (4.7.14). Such techniques require the balancing of the coefficients of trigonometric functions. $x(t)$ is presented as a sum of expressions involving $\sin \alpha t$ and $\cos \alpha t$, where α is an integer submultiple of ω. The only way to cancel out the $\sin \omega t$ in the right-hand side of Eq. (4.7.14) is to raise $\sin \alpha t$ to a power ω/α. Thus high-order subharmonics can result only when $g(x)$ is close to a high power of x.

The phenomenon of subharmonic entrainment (or frequency demultiplication) has been observed in a number of experiments involving diurnal rhythms. Bruce [Bru-I] reports some very striking cases: A mouse (Peromyscus) was exposed to light–dark cycles of 6:6*

---

* This notation denotes 6 hours of light followed by 6 hours of dark.

(i.e., a period of 12 hours), 4:4 (period of 8 hours), and 2:4 (period of 6 hours). In all cases entrainment to a period of 24 hours was observed. A cockroach (Leucophaea) [Rob-2] was entrained to the same period by a 2:2 cycle (4-hour period). A hamster was not only entrained to 24 hours by periods of 6 (2:4) and 4 (1:3) hours but also to 25 hours by a period of 6.25 hours (2:4.25). Entrainment failed only when the period was reduced to 2 hours (1:1).

These results indicate entrainment up to the sixth subharmonic. This implies a highly nonlinear system in terms of the discussion of the previous paragraph or, possibly, a pulse entrainment mechanism of the type given by Eq. (4.7.3). The discussion of the previous section about entrainment by skeleton photoperiods includes also a case of subharmonic entrainment; namely, the one caused by a pair of pulses 12 hours apart.

4.8 Bibliographical Notes

The mathematical tools for studying entrainment of nonlinear oscillators can be found in any of many advanced texts on the theory of nonlinear systems [And-I, Min-I]. Wever [Wev-3, Wev-4] has presented examples of computer simulation of such systems in relation to biological clocks. A detailed analysis of the relation between amplitude and limits of entrainment can be found in particular in the texts by Minorsky [Min-I], Haag [Haa-I], and Butenin [But-I].

Cases of studies of entrainment of circadian oscillators are too many to mention. The paper by Bruce [Bru-1] gives a comprehensive list of the earlier works, while a brief review can be found in the book by Bünning [Bün-A]. The following references are papers describing quantitative results and/or less typical phenomena like subharmonic entrainment, oscillatory free runs, etc. [Asc-1, Asc-3, Edm-5, Enr-1, Esk-3, Hof-2, Hof-4, Hof-5, Hof-6, Hof-8, Hös-1, Hös-2, Kra-1, Lam-1, Min-1, Pit-5, Pit-6, Pit-7, Rob-2, Swa-1].

Many studies on entrainment have been made in the context of photoperiodism, i.e., the change in behavior caused by a change in the length of the day. The relative phase of the circadian clock with respect to the light cycle is obviously a function of the duration of the light period, and this could be used by the organism to change its mode of behavior [Wit-A, Adk-1, Adk-2, Asc-9, Bün-2, Far-1, Far-2, Hal-3, Hep-1, Men-1, Min-1, Pit-2, Pit-5, San-1, Und-1, etc.]. However, some doubt has been cast on this mechanism in view of recent experiments [Pit-11, Pit-12].

CHAPTER 5

The Dynamics of Circadian Oscillators

5.1 Introduction

We have followed up to this point two somewhat distinct approaches. In one we have used the phase response curve to study entrainment of a certain circadian rhythm by pulses of light. In the other we have used the theory of weakly nonlinear systems to study the response of biological rhythms to "weak" stimuli. It would be interesting to see how these two approaches can be tied together and also investigate the effects on biological oscillators of nonperiodic stimuli. There is a considerable amount of experimental data about the latter and efforts have been made in predicting the latter behavior from the features of the phase response curve for a given rhythm.

It turns out that the two types of behavior are independent in the sense that it is quite easy to construct simple models which fit two distinct sets of specifications about their response to light stimuli of short duration (or generally time varying) and to the constant light intensity of their environment. This analysis is carried out further with computer simulation of various models.

This conclusion has certain implications about the designing of experiments of biological rhythms. If the effect of light intensity on the free-run period could be deduced formally from a PRC, then the effort in conducting both types of experiments is not justified. If, on the other hand, one set of data cannot be deduced formally from the other, then it is worthwhile to conduct both kinds of experiments.

As we have seen in the previous chapters the shape of the PRC differs little from organism to organism, and it is what one would expect for enabling an organism to be quickly entrained by light and dark cycles. There seems to be no such survival value for the relation between free-run period and light intensity. Hence the latter may provide information about the structure of the circadian oscillator.

Finally we present a set of results which deal with stopping the oscillation by bringing the state of the system close to the singularity and with starting the oscillation from that state.

5.2 Dependence of the Period of an Oscillator on Constant Environmental Factors

We saw in Chapter 3 how exposure of an oscillator to temporary changes of its environment results in phase shifts. Phase response curves (PRC) describe the relation between the latter and the time when the "disturbance" occurs. One would expect that periodic application of such stimuli would result in entrainment, and in the previous chapter we saw how this is indeed the case. A more interesting question is whether one can deduce the effect of long-duration changes in the environment from the PRC of an oscillator. Intuitively one expects that a stimulus which always causes a phase advance when applied temporarily (by presumably speeding up the oscillation) will cause an increase in frequency if it is applied continuously. However the PRC curves of Chapter 3 show that usually a temporary application of a stimulus causes both advances and delays. Thus the prediction of its long-term effects is not trivial. The problem is further complicated by questions of adaptation. Most biological receptors possess that property, and therefore it is natural to expect that the effect of stimuli of long duration will be less pronounced than the effect of stimuli of short duration. The exact meaning of the terms "short" and "long" can be expressed in terms of the time constants of the adaptation mechanism. Generally, most receptors adapt within a few minutes, and therefore stimuli of duration of, say, one hour can be treated as long. On the other hand there might be adaptation at higher levels. We prefer to use the term *compensation* for such a process. Typically it might involve a complex set of reactions directly affecting the oscillator itself.

A rather obvious case of compensation occurs in the response of plants or cold-blooded (poikilothermal) animals to changes in the temperature of their environment. The period of the circadian rhythm shows hardly any dependence on the (constant) temperature of the environment. Usually the period changes by less than 5% for temperature changes up to 10°C. However a sudden increase of the temperature by 10°C can cause phase shifts of up to 4 hours [Bün-A, Zim-1, Zim-2]. We will discuss this phenomenon in more detail in the next chapter.

In contrast to temperature, the effects of environmental illumination are more pronounced, even if the light intensity remains constant over many periods. There is a wealth of experimental results, and there even seems to be some relation between the form of the dependence of the period of oscillation on the ambient light intensity and the behavior of the organism. Aschoff [Asc-1] has expressed this dependence by the so-called circadian rule:

"In diurnal (day-active) organisms their period is a decreasing function of light intensity while in nocturnal (night-active) organisms the period is an increasing function of light intensity."

In particular, the period of the oscillations seems to depend linearly on the logarithm of the light intensity [Bün-A, Hof-1, Hof-3]. Although there are too many exceptions to accept the behavioral implications of the rule [Cai-1, Erk-1, Esk-1, Hof-3, Hof-7, Hof-10, Rob-1], still the dependence of the period upon light intensity is an undisputed phenomenon.

We will discuss in the sequence the relation between PRC's and the circadian rule.

Bünning [Bün-A] has stated that the relative duration of the part of the cycle where a light stimulus causes advances versus the part where delays are caused can be used to predict whether a long-duration stimulus will cause an increase or a decrease in the period. This reasoning seems to be applicable in the case of the leaf movement rhythm of the bean plant, *Phaseolus multiflorus*. The period of oscillations in far-red light is shorter than in dark, while a 3-hour pulse of far-red light causes phase advances over most of the cycle. On the other hand, the period in red light is longer than in dark while a 3-hour pulse of red light causes delays over most of the cycle [Bün-A, Bün-3]. However the interpretation of the effects of far-red light has been disputed [Hal-4]. In addition one can come up with examples where the overall interpretation is not valid.

The PRC of the eclosion rhythm of Drosophila pseudoobscura (see Fig. 3.3.2) has comparable zones of advances of delays. However continuous light causes damping of the oscillation. The biochemical oscillator described in Section 3.5 also shows fairly "balanced" PRC's for light pulses of short duration (Fig. 3.6.2). However its period is a linearly increasing function of the "light effect" (Fig. 5.2.1). Bünning's argument seems to be valid only when one considers PRC's for light pulses of durations close to half a period (Figs. 3.3.6 and 3.6.3). But of course the value of a prediction is diminished if the two stimuli are very similar to each other.

In the next three sections we will present examples which will further

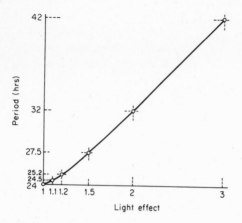

Fig. 5.2.1. Period of oscillations as a function of the light
effect expressed as a ratio of the
values of B_2 in Eq. (3.6.5) [Pav-9].

demonstrate the lack of strong interdependence between PRC's and the
circadian rule. In particular we will describe mathematical models whose
response to continuous stimuli is varied but all have the same PRC's.
As we mentioned in the introduction, such a discussion is of more than
academic interest.

The fact that the circadian rule does not seem to be a valid generalization is one additional argument in favor of studying the effects of
light intensity on the free-run period. (See also Section 5.5.)

5.3 Mathematical Formulation of a Model for Biological Oscillators

The investigation of the relationship between PRC's and the circadian
rule can be helped by using a concrete mathematical model. We have
already seen such a model in Section 3.6. However in that case we dealt
with a system of very specific structure, and the generality of results
derived from its study can be challenged. It would be desirable to use a
simpler model whose structure is specified at a minimum [Pav-4,
Pav-5]. The discussion of Section 3.4 is a beginning in that direction.
However the topological model developed there gives incomplete
information about the overall dynamics of the system. Here we go one
step further and assume that we deal with an oscillator with a single
degree of freedom described by the following (generic) pair of nonlinear
differential equations.

$$dr/dt = f(r, s) \qquad (5.3.1)$$

$$ds/dt = g(r, s) \qquad (5.3.2)$$

where r and s are the two state variables and f and g are to be chosen so that the system of Eqs. (5.3.1) and (5.3.2) exhibits a limit cycle. For a physical system it is justified to assume that the range of values taken by r and s is not unbounded, but it is between certain limits. Moreover, from the analysis of Section 3.4, one can conclude that the zone between CT4 and CT12 corresponds to the "saturation" of one of the state variables. We choose r to be this variable and, without any loss of generality, we assume that it is always nonnegative; i.e., the "saturation level" is zero.

In order that the system described by Eqs. (5.3.1) and (5.3.2) has a limit cycle, it is necessary that the characteristic equation of its linearized form has two roots of the same sign (Section 1.2). Let r_c, s_c be the coordinates of the critical point; i.e.,

$$f(r_c, s_c) = 0 \tag{5.3.3}$$

$$g(r_c, s_c) = 0 \tag{5.3.4}$$

Using the notation of Section 1.2 we have the following equations for the linearized form:

$$dr/dt = f_r \cdot r + f_s \cdot s \tag{5.3.5}$$

$$ds/dt = g_r \cdot r + g_s \cdot s \tag{5.3.6}$$

The two roots will be the same sign if

$$f_r g_s - f_s g_r > 0 \tag{5.3.7}$$

Inequality (5.3.7) is a necessary (but not sufficient) condition for a limit cycle [see Section 1.2, Eq. (1.2.14), and condition (2)].

If the critical point is asymptotically stable, then there must be a region R around it so that, if the point (r_0, s_0) belongs to R, then the trajectory starting from it tends to (r_c, s_c) for $t \to \infty$. In terms of the model for the circadian oscillator it would mean that, once the state of the system is in R, the oscillation would damp out and could be started again only by some outside stimulus.

Such a system would be rather undesirable as a biological regulator unless the likelihood that its state was brought in R was very small. There is some experimental evidence in favor of small region of attraction around the singularity but it is rather inconclusive. We will discuss this question again in Section 5.6. For the overall dynamic response of the system a good first approximation could be achieved by ignoring R (if indeed it is a region not easily attainable) and assuming that the critical point is unstable; i.e., the roots of the characteristic equation have nonnegative real parts. If they are zero, this would imply the existence of a center and the possibility of more than one periodic trajectory, depending on the initial conditions.

This is an unlikely occurrence in view of the superposition properties of the PRC's discussed in Chapters 3 and 4. Also such systems are structurally unstable, in the sense that very small changes in their parameters can result in drastic changes of their behavior [And-I]. Finally, the discussion of Section 1.7 shows that the periods along each trajectory will in general be different.

Therefore the real parts should be positive or, in other words,

$$f_r + g_s > 0 \qquad (5.3.8)$$

It is also preferable that the curves $f(r, s) = 0$ and $g(r, s) = 0$ do not have more than one intersection, because that would imply the existence of another critical point in the plane and it would offer the possibility for large enough disturbances to move the system outside of the attraction region of the limit cycle and hence damp out the oscillation. (Such a situation has occurred in a previous model proposed by Wever [Wev-1, Wev-2, Wev-4].) The above conditions are fairly general and they should be satisfied by any system which is a candidate for a model of the basic circadian oscillator.

We now want to choose one that will present a limit cycle which will include a segment of the axis $r = 0$ as part of its trajectory (in order to simulate the sector CT 4–12). A very simple approach is to design the system in such a way so that the critical point is an unstable focus (i.e., we rule out now the possibility of an unstable node). Then all trajectories would eventually intersect the axis $r = 0$. There will exist one trajectory tangent to it, and the system will leave this axis on it (Point A) to meet it again at B (Fig. 5.3.1). The curve $ACBA$ will be a limit cycle provided the motion along the s axis is from right to left. It will be a stable limit cycle because any trajectory starting in the interior of the region enclosed by the curve $ACBA$ will eventually meet the segment BA and any one starting outside it will meet the s axis ($r = 0$) and then the limit cycle at B. The necessary and sufficient conditions for a focus is given by Eq. (1.2.15); namely,

$$(f_r - g_s)^2 + 4f_s g_r < 0 \qquad (5.3.9)$$

Note that this implies Eq. (5.3.7), which can now be omitted from the list of necessary conditions for a limit cycle. For $r = 0$, Eq. (5.3.2) becomes

$$ds/dt = g(0, s) \qquad (5.3.10)$$

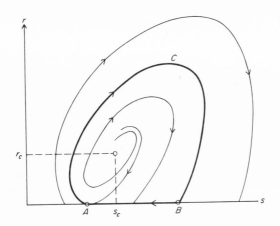

FIG. 5.3.1. Phase plane plot of trajectories of the system of Eqs. (5.3.1) and (5.3.2).

and the motion will be from right to left (i.e., s will be decreasing) if and only if

$$g(0, s) < 0 \qquad (5.3.11)$$

Conditions (5.3.8), (5.3.9), and (5.3.11), plus the requirement that the system of Eqs. (5.3.3) and (5.3.4) have a unique solution in the first quadrant, guarantee the existence of a unique stable limit cycle, as shown in Fig. 5.3.1. Note that the system described in Section 3.6 has a limit cycle of similar form (Fig. 3.6.1). In order to take into account the effects of variable light intensity we have to modify our previous description and devise a formal mechanism by which light affects r. The simplest possibility is to rewrite Eq. (5.3.1) as

$$dr/dt = f(r, s) - K \cdot l \qquad (5.3.12)$$

where K is a sensitivity coefficient and l represents the light intensity. If l is greater (in absolute value) than the maximum of $f(r, s)$ (with respect to both r and s on the limit cycle) divided by K, then dr/dt will be negative and r will start decreasing as soon as the light is turned on. The rate of decrease will be larger for larger l, and in such a case r may be zero in a very short time. This corresponds to the model of Section 3.4. For a given (small) pulse duration any increase of the light intensity beyond this level will not affect the shape of the phase response curve.

If the light stimulus is not very strong, then the change in the value of r will not necessarily be such that $\dot{r} = 0$, but r will have a value somewhere in between. This new value can be found approximately as follows: If the duration of the stimulus is very short, then the pulse can be approximated by a delta function of area L ($L = l \cdot \varDelta t$, where $\varDelta t$ is the pulse duration) occurring at time t. Then, integrating Eq. (5.3.12) from $t - 0$ to $t + 0$, one obtains

$$r(t + 0) = r(t - 0) - K \cdot L$$

After the removal of light the motion will resume according to the pattern shown in Fig. 5.3.1 and the system will be back on the limit cycle after a certain time interval. Equation (5.3.12) allows us to study the behavior of the system under constant illumination. The term $-Kl$ can be incorporated in f and this will have as a result movement of the curve $f(r, s) = 0$ in the direction shown in Fig. 5.3.2a and b. One can

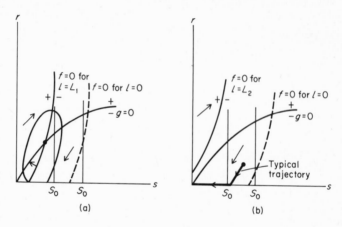

FIG. 5.3.2.   Change of the phase plane portrait under the influence of light: $L_1 < L_2$.

see that the limit cycle (if it exists) will move towards lower r. For higher intensities the curve $f(r, s) = 0$ may move so far that it does not intersect the curve $g(r, s) = 0$ in the first quadrant. This means that the system will not have a singular point there, and therefore a limit cycle cannot exist.

Figure 5.3.2a shows the trajectories corresponding to low light intensity (or low sensitivity). A limit cycle exists and it is displaced only to the left.

Figure 5.3.2b shows a case where no limit cycle can exist. This corresponds to high light intensities (or high sensitivity).

The negative term Kl in Eq. (5.3.12) results in a decrease in dr/dt. If light is applied during a part of the limit cycle when dr/dt is positive, its effect will be to slow down the oscillation. If it is applied during a part when dr/dt is negative, its effect will be to speed up the oscillation. Thus the PRC will present both delays and advances.

On the other hand, it is not clear what the period would be on a new limit cycle (as shown in Fig. 5.3.2a). The uncertainty is due to the fact that it has been moved to a different part of the phase plane and its period will be determined primarily by the form of the functions $f(r, s)$ and $g(r, s)$.

The situation may be further complicated by assuming that the coefficient K in Eq. (5.3.12) is not constant but depends on the light intensity. In this way we are led to consider an adaptive system if K takes small values for high light intensities and large values for low light intensities. It is reasonable to assume that the change in the values of K is not instantaneous but shows a time lag with respect to the change of the light intensity. This can be described in most simple terms by a differential equation of the following form:

$$\tau \, dK/dt + K = G(l) \tag{5.3.13}$$

where τ is a time constant and $G(l)$ is a decreasing function of l.

This feature will be very prominent when the system is exposed to light for periods much longer than τ, and it offers an explanation for the behavior of the *Drosophila* eclosion rhythm. It is known that, although the rhythm is damped in continuous light, eclosion continues in irregular intervals. If we assume the existence of the adaptive mechanism, the oscillator is damped only temporarily, but as soon as K reaches a low enough value the oscillation starts again. Since τ may have different values for different individuals, one expects that the synchrony among various oscillators is lost and the apparent loss of rhythmicity is observed.

Equation (5.3.12) also indicates the possibility of entrainment if the product Kl varies periodically with time.

5.4   The Independence between the Phase Response Curve and the Effects of Light on the Free-Run Period

The simplest form of the model of the previous section occurs when $f(r, s)$ and $g(r, s)$ are linear. Then Eqs. (5.3.12) and (5.3.2) become

$$dr/dt = a_{11}r + a_{12}s + b, \qquad r \geqslant 0$$

$$ds/dt = a_{21}r + a_{22}s$$

b represents a bias and the effect of light. It can be easily seen that there is no loss of generality if we assume $a_{11} = a_{21} = 1$. [Indeed divide both sides of the first equation by a_{11} and of the second by a_{21} and define new variables $t' = a_{11}t$ and $s' = (a_{11}/a_{21})s$; then the resulting equations in r, s' and t' have this property.] Thus we may simplify the above equations as

$$dr/dt = r - cs + b, \qquad r \geqslant 0 \tag{5.4.1}$$

$$ds/dt = r - as \tag{5.4.2}$$

The critical point is located at

$$r_c = ab/(c - a) \tag{5.4.3}$$

$$s_c = b/(c - a) \tag{5.4.4}$$

while conditions (5.3.8) and (5.3.9) now become

$$1 - a > 0 \tag{5.4.5}$$

$$4c > (1 + a)^2 \tag{5.4.6}$$

The point where the limit cycle meets the s axis has coordinate

$$s^* = b/c \tag{5.4.7}$$

Equations (5.4.1) and (5.4.2) can be solved explicitly to obtain

$$r(t) = \frac{ab}{c - a}\left[1 - \frac{\sin(\omega t + \psi)}{\sin \psi}e^{-\mu t}\right] \tag{5.4.8}$$

and

$$s(t) = \frac{b}{c} + \frac{b}{c - a}\left\{1 - \frac{e^{-\mu t}}{\sin \psi}\left[\omega \cos(\omega t + \psi) + (1 - \mu)\sin(\omega t + \psi)\right]\right\} \tag{5.4.9}$$

where

$$\mu = (1 - a)/2 \tag{5.4.10}$$

$$\omega = \left[c - \left(\frac{a + 1}{2}\right)^2\right]^{1/2} \tag{5.4.11}$$

and

$$\tan \psi = \mu/\omega \tag{5.4.12}$$

One can readily verify that

$$r(0) = 0, \qquad dr/dt\,|_{t=0} = 0$$

and

$$s(0) = b/c$$

In other words, at $t = 0$ the system is at the point A as shown in Fig. 5.3.1. The time T_{AB} required to reach the point B can be found from Eq. (5.4.8) by setting the LHS equal to zero and solving with respect to t. Obviously the solutions of this equation (and hence T_{AB}) *do not depend on b* but only on a and c (through the quantities ψ, ω, and μ). The quantity in braces in Eq. (5.4.9) does not also depend on b, and therefore the value $s(T_{AB})$ can be expressed as

$$s(T_{AB}) = b/c + [b/(c - a)] \cdot F \qquad (5.4.13)$$

where F is independent of b. During the motion from B to A the system obeys the differential equation

$$ds/dt = - as \qquad (5.4.14)$$

and the time to transverse that interval is given by

$$T_{BA} = (1/a) \log[s(0)/s(T_{AB})]$$

or

$$T_{BA} = \frac{1}{a} \log \left\{ \frac{1}{1 + [c/(c - a)]F} \right\} \qquad (5.4.15)$$

This quantity is also independent of b, and therefore we have the following result:

The period of oscillations on the limit cycle of the system described by Eqs. (5.4.1) and (5.4.2) is independent of b. In terms of the model for circadian rhythms this means that the period does not depend on the light intensity.

On the other hand, the system does have nonzero phase response curves. This is because any *temporary* change in b results in deviations from the limit cycle and the system meets the s axis at a point other than B. The cancellations of Eqs. (5.4.8) and (5.4.15) are not valid any more. Consider for example moving the point C to D as in Fig. 5.4.1 and let that time be negligible in comparison to the time T_{CBD} required to go from C to D through B along the limit cycle. (This can be easily achieved for a sufficiently large temporary increase in b.) If C is before the triggering of the timing event (see Section 3.1), then a delay equal to T_{DAC} (the time required to go from D to C through A) is observed. If C is after the timing event, then an advance equal to T_{CBD} is observed. Actually the system behaves very much like the model of Section 3.4 and it can reproduce the PRC of the eclosion rhythm of Drosophila pseudoobscura (Fig. 3.2.2). It can also be entrained by light pulses in the manner described in the previous chapter.

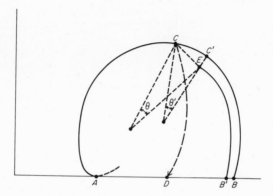

Fig. 5.4.1. Phase plane plot of the effects of changes in a parameter on a system which has a limit cycle with period independent of the value of that parameter. See text for explanation.

"Weak" light can also cause phase shifts. Moving C to E results in a trajectory $CEB'A$ instead of $CC'BB'A$. From the elementary theory of linear systems, we know that the time from E to B' equals that from C' to B. The times for C to C' and C to E are about equal (they are proportional to the angles θ and θ'). Thus the disturbance saves the time from B to B' and thus causes a phase advance. In the next section we show such examples obtained by computer simulation. Also additional examples illustrating entrainment by sinusoidal stimuli.

We thus have a system which can be phase shifted and entrained by light stimuli but its period is independent of the constant light intensity! Not only is this the case but also the PRC's for strong-light increases obtained for different "background" light intensities are identical. (We leave the proof of that as an exersize for the reader.)

Although it is highly unlikely that any biological clock has a mechanism as simple as the one of Eqs. (5.4.1) and (5.4.2), there is no reason to argue against the possibility of other, more complex systems sharing the same property. In any case, we have an example which shows that the PRC's provide no information whatsoever about the behavior of the system under constant environmental conditions.

A wider variety of responses can be obtained by adding a nonliner term in Eq. (5.4.1) [Pav-4, Pav-5]. This will make the period dependent on b but will have little effect on the shape of the PRC's. We will study one such particular case where Eq. (5.4.1) is replaced by

$$dr/dt = r + b - cs - ds^2, \quad r \geqslant 0 \qquad (5.4.16)$$

All the coefficients are assumed to be positive.

Conditions (5.3.8) and (5.3.9) for this system are equivalent to

$$1 - a > 0 \tag{5.4.17}$$

$$(1 - a)^2 < 4[(c - a)^2 + 4bd]^{1/2} \tag{5.4.18}$$

We also have

$$r_c = (a/2b)\{a - c + [(c - a)^2 + 4bd]^{1/2}\} \tag{5.4.19}$$

$$s_c = (1/2b)\{a - c + [(c - a)^2 + 4bd]^{1/2}\} \tag{5.4.20}$$

and

$$s^* = (1/2b)\{-c + [c^2 - 4bd]^{1/2}\} \tag{5.4.21}$$

where s^* is the point of contact denoted by A in Fig. 5.3.1.

The effect of the nonlinear term is more pronounced for large values of s. If d is positive, then a high negative term is added in the branch CB of Fig. 5.4.1 and this tends to speed up the process. A decrease in the value of b [corresponding to an increase in light intensity according to Eq. (5.3.15)] would move the limit cycle to smaller values of s and therefore the "speed up" will be less. Hence the period will increase with a decrease in b; i.e., an increase in the light intensity. Thus the model follows the circadian rule like a typical nocturnal animal.

However this is not the only way of modifying the law of the change of the period with light intensity in the above model. For a given positive d one could assume that the dependence of b on L is not always the same. If b is a decreasing function of L, then the system will also model a diurnal organism. But in this case the PRC's will be different. Although a qualitative description of the changes is possible we prefer to proceed with some concrete examples obtained from computer simulation.

5.5   Computer Simulation of Models for the Circadian Clock

A series of computer simulations was carried out in order to illustrate the concepts discussed in the previous sections. These were implemented through a FORTRAN program, first on an IBM 7094 machine and then on an IBM 360/91 [Pav-4, Pav-5, Pav-7]. The basic equations of the model were the following:

$$dr/dt = r - cs - ds^2 + b - x, \quad r \geqslant 0 \tag{5.5.1}$$

$$ds/dt = r - as \tag{5.5.2}$$

where b is a constant "bias" term and x represents a variable light intensity. Whenever s crossed upwards the value s_c [given by Eq. (5.4.20)] a timing event was triggered.

The results of the simulation are summarized below.

(1) Effect of b on a piecewise linear system. For $a = 0.5$, $c = 0.6$, $d = 0.0$, and $x = 0.0$, b was given the values 0.2, 0.5, 1.0, and 4.0. In all cases the period was equal to 28.10, although the location of the limit cycles on the s–r plane was different. For the same values of a, d, and x, but with $c = 0.7$, the period was equal to 16.80 for $b = 0.5$ and $b = 4.0$.

(2) Effect of b in the presence of the quadratic term. Table 5.5.1 shows this dependence for $a = 0.5$, $c = 0.7$, and $x = 0.0$. It is seen that the higher the value of d the stronger is the dependence.

TABLE 5.5.1

PERIODS OF OSCILLATION FOR VARIOUS VALUES OF b AND d

d	$b = 0.5$	$b = 4.0$	Ratio of periods
0.00	16.80	16.80	1.000
0.01	13.85	10.00	1.385
0.10	9.57	5.95	1.610
0.50	6.70	3.95	1.695

(3) Entrainment by periodic values of x. Table 5.5.2 shows one set of results obtained for $a = 0.5$, $c = 0.7$, $d = 4.0$, and various values of d. The input x was of the form

$$x(t) = L[1 + \tfrac{1}{2} \sin(2\pi/T_1)t] \tag{5.5.3}$$

E means entrainment, TE tendency towards entrainment (in a run consisting of about 10 cycles), SE subharmonic entrainment with the period in parentheses, NE no entrainment, and D damping of the macroscopic oscillation (the oscillations were actually going on but failed to cross the threshold for the timing event). It is seen that the higher L is the broader are the limits of entrainment, as is expected from the discussion of Section 4.2. The value of b seems also to be positively correlated with the latter quantity but not as strongly. Thus for $b = 0.01$ a period equal to 149% of T_0 (14.90 vs 10.00) fails to entrain for $L = 2$ while for $b = 0.50$ entrainment occurs for a period equal to 170% of T_0 (6.70 vs 3.95).

TABLE 5.5.2

RESULTS OF COMPUTER SIMULATION OF ENTRAINMENT

d	T_0	L	T_1 and results of entrainment (in parentheses, T_1 in % of T_0)							
			10.60	12.70	14.80	15.00	16.90	18.00	21.00	24.00
		1	NE	NE	TE	E	E	E	TE	NE
0.00	16.80									
		4	SE(21.20)	TE	E	E	E	E	E	E
			6.25	7.50	8.75	9.35	10.00	11.20	13.05	14.90
		2	SE(12.50)	NE	NE	E	E	E	TE	NE
0.01	10.00									
		4	SE(12.50)	SE(15.00)	TSE(17.30)	E	E	E	E	E
			3.10	3.70	4.30	4.90	5.00	6.00	7.00	8.00
		2	TSE(6.80)	SE(7.40)	NE	NE	NE	E	E	E
0.10	5.95									
		4	D	D	D	D	D	D	E	E
			2.50	3.00	3.50	4.00	5.60	6.70	7.80	8.90
		2	SE(5.00)	SE(9.00)	E	E	E	E	TE	NE
0.50	3.95									
		4	D	D	D	D	E	E	E	E

Note also that the asymmetry of the limits of entrainment around T_0 is an artifact. In Section 4.2 we have seen that the critical quantity is $|\omega_0{}^2 - \omega_1{}^2|$; i.e.,

$$Q(T_1) = |(1/T_0)^2 - (1/T_1)^2| \qquad (5.5.4)$$

For $b = 0$ we have

$$Q(14.80) = 0.100 \cdot 10^{-2}$$

and

$$Q(21.00) = 0.040 \cdot 10^{-2}$$

The latter quantity is the smaller of the two, although the corresponding value of T_1 is farthest from T_0.

For one set of values of $a = 0.5$, $b = 1.0$, $c = 0.6$, and $d = 1.0$ an additional series of tests were performed involving longer runs in order to see whether reproduction of oscillatory free runs was possible. In this case the input x was given by

$$x(t) = L[1 + y \sin(2\pi/T_1)t] \qquad (5.5.5)$$

TABLE 5.5.3

RESULTS OF COMPUTER SIMULATION OF ENTRAINMENT

		Nonadaptive system for $q = 1.5^a$		
L	T_2 (hr)	T_L(hr)	T_{obs} (hr)	T_{pred} (hr)
0.2	25.1	25.6	502	550
0.3	26.2	26.5	288	286
0.5	27.9	28.5	168	172

		Adaptive system for $q = 1.5^a$		
L	T_2 (hr)	T_L (hr)	T_{obs} (hr)	T_{pred} (hr)
0.2	~25	25.5	Data not precise enough	T_2 not precise enough
0.3	25.7	26	360	363
0.5	26.5	27	265	255

Nonadaptive system for $q = 9$

	T_1 (hr)				
L	15.5	18	20.5	23	15.5
0.2	NE	NE	NE	E	E
0.4	SE	NE	E	E	E
0.6	SE	SE	TE	E	E

Nonadaptive system for $q = 1.5$

	T_1 (hr)				
L	15.5	18	20.5	23	25.5
0.1	25	25	25	25	25
0.2	25.5	25.5	25.5	25	26
0.4	27	27	27	27	26.5

Adaptive system for $q = 9$

	T_1 (hr)				
L	15.5	18	20.5	23	25.5
0.1	NE	NE	NE	TE	TE
0.2	NE	NE	NE	TE	TE
0.4	NE	NE	NE	E	E

^{a} $T_1 = 24$ hours in all cases.

In some of the tests the values of x were multiplied by a factor k given by the following relation:

$$dk/dt + k = 1/[1 + x(t)] \qquad (5.5.6)$$

This corresponds to an adaptive system. Two values of y were used: 0.2 and 0.8. In the first case the ratio q between the maximum and minimum value of $x(t)$ is 1.5 and, in the second, 9. The results are summarized in Table 5.5.3, where for illustrative purposes the periods are expressed in hours. T_L is the one corresponding to L when $y = 0$, while T_2 is the average value observed. Then

$$T_{\text{pred}} = T_1 T_2 /|\, T_1 - T_2\,| \qquad (5.5.7)$$

is the period of the beats. Figures 5.5.1 and 5.5.2 show results of the simulation where the "period of activity" was taken as that for which s exceeds a given threshold. Not only are oscillatory free runs present but their quantitative behavior is according to Eq. (5.5.7). Thus the model

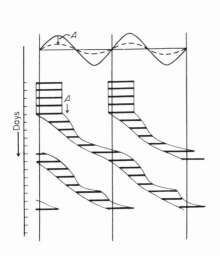

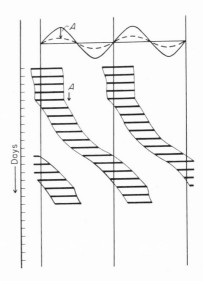

FIG. 5.5.1. Computer simulation of the experiment of Fig. 1 for $E = 0.5$ and a nonadaptive system. Point A denotes the change of the variation of the input, and it clearly results in passing from entrainment to frequency fluctuations [Pav-7].

FIG. 5.5.2. As Fig. 5.5.1, but for an adaptive system [Pav-7].

of Eqs. (5.5.1) and (5.5.2) simulates the behavior described in Section 4.4 (see also Fig. 4.4.1).

(4) Phase response curves. Figure 5.5.3 shows a set of PRC's obtained for $a = 0.5$, $b = 1.0$, $c = 0.6$, and $d = 1.0$ and $x = L$ for an interval equal to 0.2 units of time. Figure 5.5.4 shows a family of such

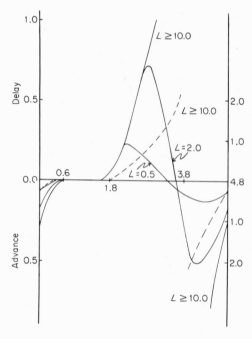

FIG. 5.5.3.   Response curves for light pulses of various intensities L and short duration (0.2). For $L \geqslant 10$, the response curves are identical. Because of the much larger phase shifts such a curve is replotted (broken line) in a smaller scale (shown on the right-hand side of the graph) [Pav-4, Pav-5].

curves for the same parameters but variable durations ($L = 5$). Thus the model simulates the PRC's discussed in the previous chapters. However the value of d is quite high and a series of additional tests were carried out to investigate the effect of this parameter on the shape of the PRC. Table 5.5.4 summarizes these results. In all cases, $a = 0.5$, $b = 4.0$, $c = 0.7$, and $x = L$ for 0.25 units of time. The maximum delay and advance are listed as well as the type of the PRC: with discontinuity (D) as in Fig. 5.5.3 for $L \geqslant 10$ or without (C) as in Fig. 5.5.3 for $L = 2$. It is seen that the amount of phase shift is, in general, an increasing

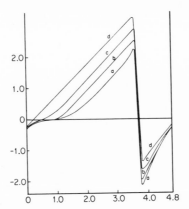

FIG. 5.5.4. Response curves for variable durations as follows: a, 0.8; b, 1.2; c, 1.6; d, 2.0; intensity, 5.0 [Pav-4, Pav-5].

function of d. Certain small discrepancies can be explained by the fact that the period was scanned in large steps and therefore the values found are not the real extrema of a PRC but approximations to them. However, it should be emphasized that the relative duration of the pulse also increases with d. Thus 0.25 is only 1.5% of the period for $d = 0$ but 6.4% for $d = 0.5$. Nevertheless there are appreciable phase shifts, even in the case where the period of the system depends very little or not at all on x.

The obvious conclusion of these tests is that it is quite easy to develop models which simulate many features of the circadian rhythms, and in particular they can handle independently the circadian rule and the phase response curves.

Note that the exceptions to the circadian rule mentioned in Section 5.2 as well as additional experimental evidence [Kra-1, Nat-1] indicate natural examples of this independence.

TABLE 5.5.4

PRC's FOR VARIOUS VALUES OF d AND L FOR PULSE DURATION EQUAL TO 0.25 UNITS

		$L = 10$			$L = 20$			$L = 40$		
d	T_0	Max. delay	Max. advance	Type	Max. delay	Max. advance	Type	Max. delay	Max. advance	Type
0.0	16.80	1.00	0.55	C	1.75	1.10	C	3.30	3.20	C
0.01	10.00	0.80	0.50	C	1.40	1.10	C	5.35	2.60	C
0.10	5.95	1.10	0.65	C	2.55	2.05	D	2.35	2.30	D
0.50	3.95	1.80	1.55	D						

5.6   Starting and Stopping the Clock

All the models discussed in this chapter as well as in Section 3.6 have a state space with a singularity within the limit cycle. In all cases there exists a value of the light intensity I^* which, if applied for time length T^* at a point of the limit cycle C^*, will bring the state at or close to the singularity. [For a given form of $f(r, s)$ these quantities can be obtained by integrating Eq. (5.3.12).] If the singularity is stable, then oscillations will be completely damped out after the application of such an input. If it is unstable, then they will start building up again. However, for some time after the application of the stimulus, the oscillations will be of relatively small amplitude and they may fail to control the behavior of the organism. The latter may then become arrhythmic. Therefore in this case the macroscopic response will be a damping of the oscillation for the first few periods. The length of time for which the rhythm disappears may be prolonged if the controller is not just one unit but a population of mutually coupled oscillators. It can be shown that the various units can be mutually entrained and behave in many respects as a single unit (see Chapter 7). Disturbances which leave the units near the limit cycle are not affecting the synchronization among the various units as much as inputs which move the system away from an oscillatory state (e.g., at a singularity). The return to steady state from the latter will take in general a longer time. Thus arrhythmicity will be observed even if all the units are back on to their limit cycles but have not as yet mutually synchronized.

There have been two very interesting sets of experiments investigating the nature of the singularity of the oscillator controlling the eclosion rhythm of the fruitfly *Drosophila pseudoobscura*.

Zimmerman [Zim-3] has considered the question of rhythm initiation. A culture of fruitfly pupae which has been kept in constant environmental conditions will show in general aperiodic eclosion. This can be interpreted either as the result of asynchrony among individual clocks or as the result of an inoperative clock. If such a culture is exposed to a short light pulse, then a clear rhythm appears. This can be interpreted either as moving the rhythm outside a stable singularity and into the region of attraction of a limit cycle or as synchronizing the various clocks. The latter is quite possible because of the size of the phase shifts induced (Fig. 3.3.2). Using Eq. (3.4.1) on these data we find that, if the original distribution of p was uniform between 0 and 24 hours, the distribution of q will not only be limited between approximately 2 and 13 hours but it will also be peaked. Figure 5.6.1 shows (a) the phase transition curve (q vs p) and (b) the distribution of q for a uniform

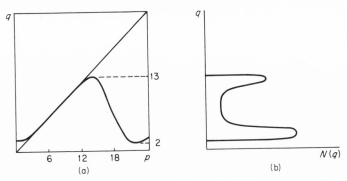

FIG. 5.6.1. (a) Phase transition curve for the light effects on the eclosion rhythm of the fruitfly *Drosophila pseudoobscura*. (b) Density $N(q)$ of flies $N(q)$ emerging at each value of q for uniform initial distribution of phases.

initial distribution of p. [Figure 5.6.2 shows how such a distribution is obtained from the phase transition curve.]

If the times of actual eclosion are normally distributed around p (with a standard deviation of, say, 1.5^h), then the final distribution of times will be closer to a unimodal form.

Therefore, barring a detailed statistical analysis of the eclosion peaks, it is not possible to distinguish between rhythm initiation and synchronization by light pulses.

On the other hand, temperature pulses cause much smaller phase shifts and hence cannot act as synchronizing agents. An increase of the ambient temperature by 8 degrees for 12 hours causes a maximum steady state phase shift of about 3.3 hours (advance). (See Fig. 6.2.2.) Figure 5.6.3 shows (a) the phase transition curve and (b) the distribution resulting from an originally uniform one.

However, experimentally such a pulse induces a very clear rhythm in a previously arrythmic population [Zim-2]. Furthermore the peaks of eclosion occur at a fixed phase in comparison to the time T of

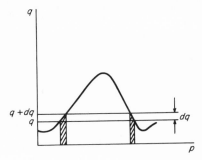

FIG. 5.6.2. The number of flies $N(q)\,dq$ emerging at the interval between q and $q + dq$ equals the sum of the shaded areas.

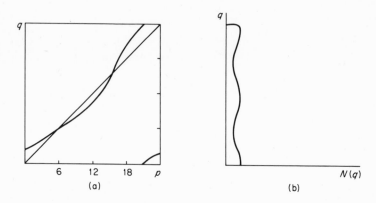

FIG. 5.6.3. (a) Phase transition curve for the temperature effects on the eclosion rhythm. (b) Density of emerging flies at each phase for initial uniform distribution.

application of the higher temperature (about 20 hours/mod 24 after T, or 7.5–8 hours/mod 24 after the end of the pulse). This would indeed be the case in rhythm initiation. If the initial state of the system is in the neighborhood of the singularity, the trajectory caused by the disturbance will show little variation and it will leave the system always near the same isochrone and therefore the relation between phase and T will be fixed. The value of this phase difference leads to the following interesting observation. Since the peak of eclosion occurs at about CT = 3.3, this relation means that the phase of the oscillator at the end of the temperature pulse was about 4–5 hours, i.e., quite close to the phase of the point B in Fig. 5.3.1 (if we assume that the zone BA corresponds to CT 4–12).

Thus, Zimmerman's experiment points strongly to the possibility of a locally stable point in the state space of the clock. However it is important to realize that this need not be the singularity. If Q is the region of attraction of the limit cycle, then it can be any point close to the boundary of Q. The singularity seems to be the more likely candidate but by no means the only one.

Winfree [Win-1, Win-3, Win-5] has conducted a series of experiments which led to "stopping" the clock by bringing it close to the singularity. His approach can best be understood by considering the isochrones as in Fig. 5.6.4 (compare also Section 3.4).

A "strong" light pulse moves points A, A_1, C, B_1, and B into A', A_1', C', B_1', B'. Points to the left of C will be delayed, the more they are closer to C. Points to the right of C will be advanced, the more they are closer to C. The corresponding part of PRC is plotted in Fig. 5.6.5. Its slope near C is equal to 2 for this particular configuration of isochrones and light effects. However the sign of the slope and the occurrence of a

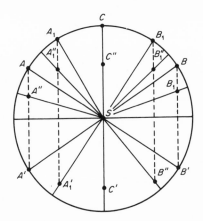

FIG. 5.6.4. Isochrones of an idealized limit cycle.

discontinuity at C are independent of the specifics as long as C' is below the singularity S.

A "weak" light pulse moves points A, A_1, C, B_1, and B into $A'' A_1'', C''$, B_1'', and B''. Points to the left of C will be delayed, the less they are closer to C. Points to the right of C will be advanced, the less they are closer to C. C itself moves on its own isochrone. The corresponding part of the PRC is plotted in Fig. 5.6.6. Its slope near C is equal to -1 for this particular configuration of isochrones and light effects. However the sign of the slope and the occurrence of a zero at C are independent of the specifics as long as C'' is above the singularity S.

The qualitative difference between the two PRC's can be used to

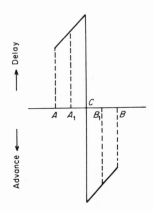

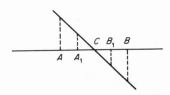

FIG. 5.6.5. Part of a PRC corresponding to strong stimuli applied to the limit cycle of Fig. 5.6.4.

FIG. 5.6.6. Part of a PRC corresponding to weak stimuli applied to the limit cycle of Fig. 5.6.4.

determine the "strength" of a light pulse which will bring the system at S or at least very close to it. Winfree found out that the system saturated very quickly to the level of light intensity, and he used the duration of the light pulse as the controlling variable. He found out that the critical interval was 50 sec. Point C corresponds to $CT = 18.8$ (i.e., 6.8 hours from the start of the night). Exposing a rhythmic culture of pupae to that stimulus at that time resulted quickly in a complete loss of the rhythm [Win-3]. One could argue that this is due to a loss of synchrony among the individual clocks rather than damping. However a detailed analysis of distributions of emergence peaks after restoration of the rhythm by light or temperature pulses argues clearly in favor of the "stopping" hypothesis [Win-3]. In particular, a repetition of Zimmerman's experiment on such an arrythmic culture resulted in the same phase of peak occurrence as the original experiment (about 8 hours after the end of the pulse). This not only favors that hypothesis* but also suggests that the initial state of the clock in Zimmerman's experiment was the singularity. That experiment definitely suggested that the initial state was not in the region of attraction of the limit cycle (this was not a necessary conclusion of Winfree's experiments in view of the observations stated in the beginning of this section). The theory of nonlinear oscillators with one degree of freedom requires that a stable or semistable point be surrounded first by an unstable limit cycle (the boundary of R) and then by a stable limit cycle. The "area" of such a region is comparatively small as demonstrated by the necessity of a critical choice of the stimulus to bring the state of the system in there. Thus models with an unstable focus as a singularity are still valid for the behavior of the system in most of the state space.

5.7   Bibliographical Notes

We have given a list of general references about circadian clocks in Chapter 2. Modeling efforts of the phenomenon started quite early. Pittendrigh's two-oscillator model [Pit-1, Pit-2, Pit-3] assumed the existence of a driver oscillator, whose dynamics were light intensity dependent, and a driven oscillator, which was affected by temperature but not by light. The model explained some of the salient features of the interaction between light and temperature stimuli but it did not attempt any quantitative analysis. A number of models on the basis of electronic and/or mathematical analogs have since been presented by a number of

---

* Some recent work has shown that this conclusion is not as strong as originally thought [Win-7].

researchers [Bar-1, Barn-1, Enr-2, Kel-1]. Wever has pointed out the connection between a number of fundamental facts about nonlinear oscillators and properties of circadian rhythms [Wev-1, Wev-2, Wev-3, Wev-4, Wev-5]. His model however suffers from overspecification [Pav-10]. It simulates rather well data from mammals but fails to produce the large phase shifts of the eclosion rhythm of *Drosophila pseudo-obscura*. Not only is this the case but it is far from clear what type of changes are necessary to extend its validity. Another class of models have dealt with qualitative descriptions of biochemical oscillators [Ehr-1, Ehr-2, Mol-1]. Again these do not go past the mechanism for producing the oscillatory behavior, and they do not offer any specific suggestions about the effects of light.

Early versions of the models described in Sections 5.3–5.5 were presented by Pavlidis in AAAS Annual Conference in 1966 (in Washington, D.C.) and have been described in two papers [Pav-4, Pav-5]. Additional models using populations of oscillators will be discussed in Chapters 7 and 8. Recently another mathematical model has been described by Johnson and Karlsson [Joh-1, Karl-1].

CHAPTER 6

Effects of Changing Environment on the Dynamics of Biological Oscillators

6.1 Introduction

We have seen in the previous chapters cases where a biological oscillator is much more sensitive to changes in its environment than in the constant values of various environmental parameters. This is hardly surprising for biological systems which are highly adaptive, except that the time constants for such "adaptation" tend to be much longer than the ones of the various sensory organs. For example, the period of a circadian oscillator is independent of the ambient temperature and also of temporary increases of less than two hours duration. However, it can be phase shifted by increases of longer durations.

All this suggests that a more complex mechanism than pure sensory adaptation may be involved. In particular, it is possible that the dynamical structure of the system incorporates this "adaptive" property. We have already such examples in Sections 5.4 and 5.5. Here we will discuss some additional forms as well as the general types of *compensation* which can allow biological oscillators to operate in this way. Since we are dealing with mechanisms intimately associated with the oscillation process itself rather than sensory adaptation, the subject is of interest in any effort to identify the structure of biological clocks. We give next a review of some relevant topics from the theory of dynamical systems and then we describe the effects of two variables, temperature and heavy water, on the dynamics of the circadian clock. They correspond to cases of qualitative different behavior.

6.2 State Variables and Parameters

Before dealing with specific examples we will make certain general observations about the response of dynamical systems to external environments. Let the following equations describe such a system:

$$S: dx/dt = f(x, a) \qquad (6.2.1)$$

where x is the state vector (of dimension n) and a is a parameter vector (of dimension m) [Oga-I, Ros-A, Zad-I]. The essential difference between x and a is that the value of the latter is not affected by the system itself. Let A be a subset of the parameter space (i.e., the set of all possible values of a) such that, if $a \in A$, then S presents a limit cycle of period $T(a)$. This notation emphasizes the fact that the value of the period depends on a. Both x and a can also be varied externally; however, the system responds to such changes in a different way.

A step change in a will result in a permanent change in the period $T(a)$. A step change in x will result in a temporary change in the trajectories, but eventually the old period will be restablished as long as the change did not take the system outside the region of attraction of the limit cycle. We can state this in simple terms by considering the addition of a chemical substance in an oscillating culture. If the substance is "consumed" by the system (this corresponds to a state variable), then the disturbance will be only temporary. If it is not (i.e., it acts as a parameter), then the disturbance will be permanent. It is obvious that the experimental testing of such distinctions can be ambiguous, and in practice one cannot always distinguish among the two alternatives. If the "rate of consumption" is slow in comparison to the duration of the experiment, it will be easy to interpret a temporary change as permanent. It may also happen that a parameter causes a significant change in the trajectories of the system but the new limit cycle has a similar period as the old one (see Sections 5.4 and 5.5).

However, mathematically the distinction is clear: one has a "jump" in the state space in the first case but not in the second.

We illustrate these concepts with the system of Eqs. (5.5.1) and (5.5.2). A sudden change in, say, r will cause the disturbance shown in Fig. 6.2.1. The dotted-line trajectory will be followed at first but then the system will return to the limit cycle. As we have already seen in Chapters 3 and 5, this will cause a phase shift but no permanent change in the period. A sudden change in x (or a decrease in b) however will cause a new period as the system will follow the $-\cdot-$ line in Fig. 6.2.1. It will also cause a phase shift as illustrated by the two sets of isochrones in the same figure but that will tend to be independent of the time of

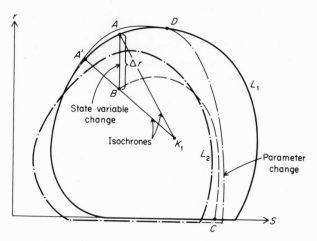

FIG. 6.2.1. A state variable change (AB) causes a phase shift (AA') but no period change (trajectory BC returns to L_1). A parameter change (D) causes a return to a different limit cycle (L_2).

the change (Fig. 6.2.2), and this is a significant difference from the previous case. In general, its absolute size will also be small for comparable changes in numerical values in the equations of the model, but this is something which is difficult to test macroscopically. However, negligible or zero phase shifts should not be unexpected.

An extreme case can be illustrated by the harmonic oscillator

$$d^2x/dt^2 + \omega^2 x = 0 \qquad\qquad (6.2.2)$$

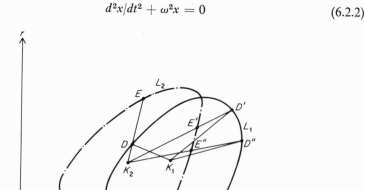

FIG. 6.2.2. A parameter change at D (isochrone K_1D) transfers the state to isochrone K_2D. Similarly for D' and D''. Phase shifts equal the difference in phase between D and E, D' and E', D'' and E''. If K_2 is close to K_1 compared to their distance from L_1 and L_2 the phase shifts will be small.

which actually does not have a limit cycle but an infinite set of periodic trajectories. We leave it as an exercise for the reader to show that:

(a)   a sudden change in x will cause a phase shift which depends on the time of the change but no change in the period;

(b)   a sudden change in the value of ω will cause a change in the period but no phase shift at all.

An environmental variable acts in general as a parameter unless the system compensates for it. We will show in the next section that temperature acts as a state variable since the system is affected only by the value $T - y$, where y is a state variable (in the strict sense) which depends on T. On the other hand, light acts as a parameter, as illustrated by the examples of Chapters 2–5. Note that the PRC's discussed are obtained by light pulses rather than steps, and thus there is no contradiction with the statement that the phase shift (if any) caused by a change in the parameter tends to be independent of the time of the change. Experiments where steps were used result in rather flat PRC's [Asc-2].

6.3   Temperature Compensation in the *Drosophila Pseudoobscura* Eclosion Rhythm

One of the first hypotheses for the temperature insensitivity of circadian rhythms was offered by Bünning [Bün-A]. He suggested that the rates of the underlying process are increasing functions of temperature in one part of the cycle and decreasing in another. A proper balance between these dependencies would produce a system with period independent of the constant ambient temperature but dependent on variations of the latter. Zimmerman [Zim-1, Zim-2] has conducted a long series of experiments involving the eclosion rhythm of the fruitfly *Drosophila pseudoobscura* which tend to contradict such a model. The following is a summary of his results.

(1)   The free-running period, τ, measured as the interval between the medians of successive eclosion peaks in constant dark and temperature, is little affected by different constant temperatures: at 10°C it is 24.7 hours, at 20°C it is 24.0 hours, and at 28°C it is 23.7 hours ($Q_{10} \cong 1.02$). Furthermore, the wave shape of the 15-min light phase response curve is essentially the same at the three temperatures.

(2)   Changes in temperature (steps and pulses) cause steady-state phase shifts: temperature steps up (20°C/28°C) give only phase advances, temperature steps down (28°C/20°C) give only phase delays, and

temperature pulses (20°C/28°C/20°C or 28°C/20°C/28°C) give both phase advances and phase delays.

(3) The magnitude and the direction (i.e., delay or advance) of the phase shift is a function of the phase of the free-running oscillation exposed to the signal. Response curves, which plot phase shifts as a function of points in the oscillation's cycle exposed to a signal, are shown for temperature steps up (20°C/28°C) and down (28°C/20°C) in Fig. 6.3.1, for 12-hour high-temperature pulses (20°C/28°C/20°C) in

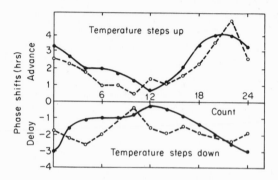

FIG. 6.3.1.   Phase shift response curves to temperature steps up from 20 to 28°C and steps down from 28 to 20°C: (○) Experimental and (●) computed results [Pav-6].

Fig. 6.3.2, and for 12-hour low-temperature pulses (28°C/20°C/28°C) in Fig. 6.3.3.

(4) An empirical relationship is found between temperature steps and pulses: the phase advance or delay generated by a 12-hour high-temperature pulse can be computed with reasonable accuracy by addition of the phase shifting effects of the steps comprising that pulse. This

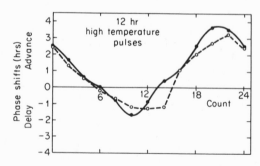

FIG. 6.3.2.   Phase shift response curves to 12-hr pulses 20°C/28°C/20°C: (○) Experimental and (●) computed results [Pav-6].

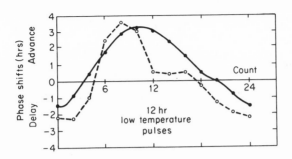

FIG. 6.3.3.   Phase shift response curves to 12-hr pulses 28°C/20°C/28°C: (○) Experimental and (●) computed results [Pav-6].

finding justifies the assumption that the phase shift normally effected by the step is accomplished within 12 hours.

It should be noted that points (1), (2), and (3) are not peculiarities of the *Drosophila* system; indeed, they are generalizations concerning the effects of temperature on circadian rhythms in poikilotherms [Bün-A, Swe-1, Wilk-1]. Point (4), the derivation of pulse phase shifts from step phase shifts, had not been previously reported. Some modifications of these statements may be warranted on the basis of recent work [Win-7], but those conclusions are not yet definitive.

Figure 6.3.1 illustrates an immediate argument against Bünning's hypothesis. If a temperature increase occurs in the zone where the rates are decreasing functions of temperature, then, according to that model, a phase delay would occur. However, the experimental data reveal only phase advances. Thus we must search for a new model.

One possible explanation involves an adaptive mechanism within the system involving a compensating factor expressed in terms of an "equivalent temperature" y. (This phenomenological expression avoids unwarranted assumptions concerning the physical mechanism. Some possible implementations will be discussed later.) The system is sensitive only to the difference $T - y$ between the temperature T and y; y follows T with some inertia. Hence a sudden increase in the temperature will accelerate all the biochemical processes of the system, and therefore a phase advance will be observed. The opposite will happen with a decrease in temperature. This model is in *qualitative* agreement with the experimental data listed above.

One additional observation by Zimmerman [Zim-1, Zim-2] was that the PRC's for 15-min light pulse were independent of the ambient temperature. This could easily be explained by the above hypothesis but not by Bünning's.

As a further test of the hypothesis a quantitative model was developed [Pav-6], described by the following equations:

$$\frac{dr}{dt} = 0.198r + 1.05 - 0.119s - 0.037s^2 \tag{6.3.1}$$

$$\frac{ds}{dt} = 0.198r - 0.099s - \mathrm{sgn}[0.198r - 0.099s] \cdot 0.09 \cdot s \left[\exp\left(\frac{T-y}{6.7}\right) - 1 \right] \tag{6.3.2}$$

$$2\frac{dy}{dt} + y = T \tag{6.3.3}$$

The simulation of this model on a computer gave the results shown in Figs. 6.3.1–6.3.3. In addition, for $T = y$, Eqs. (6.3.1) and (6.3.2) reduce to the model of Section 5.5 if the constant term in Eq. (6.3.1) is made dependent on the light intensity. Thus we have a model simulating the effects of both light and temperature on this rhythm.

Since the model is purely phenomenological we cannot draw any conclusions about the nature of y, and this is not bad in view of the limited amount of available data. However, it is desirable to consider *possible* physical systems which could account for such a mechanism. This can be done in terms of the oscillator described in Section 3.6 [Pav-9].

A look at Eqs. (3.6.1)–(3.6.3) reveals that almost all the rate constants involved enter through their ratios only. This means that the corresponding coefficients could depend much less on the temperature than the rate constants themselves. As a matter of fact the Q_{10} of the coefficients will equal the ratio of the Q_{10}'s of the rate constants. If, for example, $Q_{10}(k_7) = 2.4$ and $Q_{10}(k_6) = 2.1$, then $Q_{10}(k_7/k_6) = 1.14$. However, the oscillations could still be temperature dependent because some rate constants do not enter as ratios. Among them k_1 can be assumed temperature independent if reaction 1 is a diffusion process. Terms k_3 and k_7 enter the equations as products with the concentrations of the corresponding enzyme. Therefore one could have temperature compensation if the concentration of these enzymes were a decreasing function of temperature. This can be achieved in the following manner:

We assume that E_1 is produced as an intermediate product in the following chain of reactions:

$$W_1 \xrightarrow{k'} E_1 \xrightarrow{k''} W_2$$

where W_1 is a precursor or activator which is present in constant supply. Then in the steady state one would have

$$e_1 = (k'/k'') w_1$$

Since k', k'', and k_3 are rate constants, they can be written in the Arrhenius form,

$$k' = A' e^{-E'/RT} \tag{6.3.4}$$

$$k'' = A'' e^{-E''/RT} \tag{6.3.5}$$

$$k_3 = A_3 e^{-E_3/RT} \tag{6.3.6}$$

where A', A'', and A_3 are essentially temperature independent and E', E'', and E_3 are activation energies. Thus the temperature dependence of the quantity $k_3 e_1$ in Eq. (3.6.3) is given by

$$k_3 e_1 = A_3(A'/A'') w_1 \exp[-(E_3 + E' - E'')/RT] \tag{6.3.7}$$

This will be independent of the temperature if $E'' = E_3 + E'$ and if w_1 is independent of the temperature. A similar mechanism will lead to temperature independence of the quantity $k_7 e_2$ in Eq. (3.6.2).

In this way all the normalized coefficients of Eqs. (3.6.4)–(3.6.6) will be temperature independent, and therefore the same will be true for the behavior of the system in a constant-temperature environment. It is reasonable to assume that during a temperature change the rate constants change more rapidly than the steady-state concentrations of the enzymes. We may now investigate the effects of changes on the period and phase of the system.

Consider a sudden change in temperature from T' to T''. The reaction rate constant (e.g., k_3) will achieve its new value immediately while the concentration of the associated enzyme E_1' will require some time to reach its new steady-state value. At first, we will have $e_1 = (A'/A'')w_1 \exp[-(E' - E'')/RT']$, but eventually $e_1 = (A'/A'')w_1 \exp[-(E' - E'')/RT'']$.

We define now a "pseudotemperature" θ such that, during the transition period, the concentration of E_1 will be given by $(A'/A'')w_1 \exp[-(E' - E'')/R\theta]$. Then Eq. (6.3.7) could be written in the following form:

$$k_3 e_1 = (\text{const}) \cdot \exp[-E_3/RT''] \exp[E_3/R\theta]$$

(assuming $E' - E'' = E_3$), or

$$k_3 e_1 = (\text{const}) \cdot \exp[(E_3/RT''\theta)(T'' - \theta)] \tag{6.3.8}$$

In general the difference $T' - T''$ is much smaller than T' and Eq. (6.3.8) can be further simplified into

$$k_3 e_1 = (\text{const}) \cdot \exp[C_0(T'' - \theta] \tag{6.3.9}$$

where $C_0 = E_3/R(T'')^2$.

It is easy to see that, because of the properties of the exponential function, the change in the product $k_3 e_1$ will be more pronounced when $T'' - \theta$ is positive than when $T'' - \theta$ is negative, even if the absolute value of the difference is the same in both cases. Hence one expects greater phase shifts during temperature increases than during temperature decreases.

The phase shift will always be an advance if $T'' > T'$ and a delay if $T'' < T'$ [both B_1 and B_2 in Eqs. (3.6.5) and (3.6.6) will increase temporarily in the first case and both will decrease in the second case].

These features not only present qualitative agreement with Zimmerman's results but also Eq. (6.3.9) is of the same form as Eq. (6.3.2) which was derived in an effort to match experimental data. Furthermore it is easy to show that the amount of phase shift will depend on the circadian time. Phase response curves of this model have been derived by computer simulation [Pav-9] and are shown in Fig. 6.3.4.

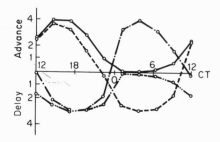

FIG. 6.3.4. Phase response curves for various temperature changes. All coordinates are in hours. (———) Curve A: sudden rise of temperature; (—·—) Curve B: sudden drop in temperature; (- - -) Curve C: a sudden rise followed by a sudden drop after half a period; (—··—) Curve D: a sudden drop followed by a sudden rise after half a period. [Pav-9].

We can summarize this discussion by stating that the clock controlling the eclosion rhythm of *Drosophila pseudoobscura* behaves as though it has a local homeostatic temperature control. One possible way of achieving this is by the involvement of enzymes whose concentrations are decreasing functions of temperature.

6.4 Temperature Compensation in Unicellular Organisms

An example of a more complex response is offered by the effects of temperature on the motility rhythm of the algae *Euglena gracilis*. Brinkmann [Bri-1, Bri-2] reports that young mixotrophic cultures have a rhythm whose period is an increasing function of temperature ($Q_{10} = 0.93$) but its phase is not affected by temperature steps. Old autotrophic cultures have a rhythm whose period (23.3 hours) is independent of the temperature ($Q_{10} = 1.00$) but its phase is shifted by a temperature step-up. Temperature step-downs have no effect on the phase.

It seems that in the first case temperature acts as a parameter while in the second as a state variable (possibly because of a feedback compensator). There is evidence that the culture medium is not the determining factor of this difference but rather the age. In particular, growing cultures show a dependence of oxygen consumption on pH, which is of a very different form than that in old cultures. Also temperature acts more drastically on the respiration in the latter ($Q_{10} \cong 3\text{--}4$) than in the former ($Q_{10} \cong 1.9$). However, respiration is rather low in old cultures, and "their metabolism is characterized by lactic acid fermentation at the expense of photosynthetic products" [Bri-1, Bri-2].

Brinkmann [Bri-1, Bri-2] has also shown that the protein synthesis inhibitor cycloheximide at concentrations 1–2 $\mu g/ml$ makes old autotrophic cultures insensitive to temperature changes while it allows phase shifts by light pulses. As a matter of fact, Feldman [Fel-1] has shown that in young cultures the amount and direction of phase shift caused by light pulses is independent of the presence of cycloheximide (at 2 $\mu g/ml$). Other experiments by Feldman give further insight into the role of this agent. The period of a culture is increased significantly by the addition of cycloheximide without any detectable phase shift [Fel-1]. The relation of period versus concentration is shown in Fig. 6.4.1 (Curve A). This is a typical case of a parameter change. This conclusion

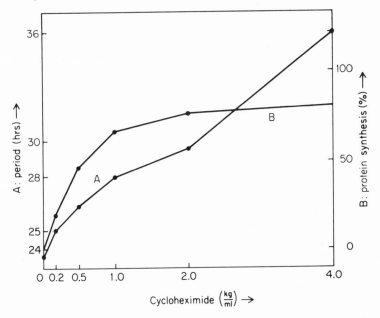

FIG. 6.4.1. Effect of cycloheximide on the period of the phototactic response of algae.

is further verified by the fact that washing out the drug restores the original period. On the other hand, the effect of cycloheximide on portein synthesis is more pronounced than its effect on the period (Fig. 6.4.1, Curve B). Thus a 77% inhibition (at 2.0 μg/ml) corresponds to a 25% period change. This is not surprising even if we assume that the rate of protein synthesis is a parameter directly involved in the clock. The relation between parameter values and period of oscillation is rarely linear (see Chapter 5). In view of these findings one might conclude that cycloheximide blocks temperature-effected phase shifts because of its inhibition of protein synthesis. However, direct experiments have shown that a temperature step-up causes an increase in protein synthesis, regardless of the presence of cycloheximide in old cultures, while in young cultures the drug keeps protein synthesis depressed [Bri-1, Bri-2]. Thus the direct effect explanation fails, and one has to admit that it is very unlikely that protein synthesis is directly participating in the clock mechanism.

The main conclusion drawn from experiments of this kind is that the temperature-compensating mechanism is inoperative in young fast-growing cultures. There the temperature acts as an external parameter.

6.5   Effects of Heavy Water

Heavy water is one of the few agents which have significant graduated effects on the period of circadian rhythms. Experiments have been performed where D_2O has been added to the drinking water of animals or to the environment of acquatic organisms. Their results seem to indicate that it acts as a parameter rather than a state variable.

There are two basic mechanisms which can explain the modification of the period of circadian rhythms. One is chemical and, in particular, the incorporation of deutereum atoms in the place of hydrogen atoms in the chemicals involved in the clock. The other is the effect of the heavy ions on the permeability of membranes. The rate of diffusion of substances used by the circadian regulator may then be affected.

Experimental evidence does not seem to be decisive in favor of either mechanism. Bruce and Pittendrigh [Bru-1] found that, if *Euglena* cells grown in H_2O are placed in a mixture of D_2O and H_2O, they loose their motility (and *a fortiori* their phototactic rhythm). On the other hand, cells which have been slowly adapted to D_2O preserve their phototactic rhythm but with a lengthening of the period (from 26.5 up to 28 hours). When they are placed back in H_2O they eventually return to a short period of about 23.5 hours. An interesting observation was that the length of the period was independent of the concentration of D_2O, as long as the latter was in excess of 20%. This behavior is consistent with the incorporation of deuterium into organic molecules. This might be a slow process, and the effect on the length period may be of quite different nature than the loss of motility during a sudden transfer of unadapted organisms into a high D_2O medium. In the case of slow adaptation the weight of the hydrogen atoms affects the period and thus acts as a *parameter* rather than a state variable. It has a permanent effect, and the fact that it is less drastic than that of a sudden transfer can be easily explained by the different nature of the mechanism involved.

A different kind of behavior was found by Enright [Enr-3] while studying the effects of heavy water in the tidal activity rhythm of an isopod, *Excirolana chiltoni*. Concentrations of D_2O in excess of 15% resulted usually in high mortality and arrhythmic activity patterns. For lower concentration an almost linear relation between length of period and D_2O concentration was observed. It seems that, on the average, the period is increased by 3 min per percent D_2O. However the number of data points was not sufficient to establish either the linear relationship or the value of the slope with a high degree of confidence. Nevertheless a functional relationship between period and D_2O concentration is evident in contrast with the all-or-none effect in *Euglena*.

Similar (proportional) effects of D_2O have been observed on the activity rhythm of the deer mouse *Peromyscus leucopus* [Sut-1], as well as on the much faster rhythms of electric activity of fish, respiratory rhythm of fish, and cardiac rhythm of clams and crabs [Enr-3]. In all these cases the effects of heavy water were reversible when the organisms were transferred in pure H_2O (or drank the same).

The time course of the change in the period is also much faster than in the *Euglena* experiments, and this is an argument in favor of the physical action of detereum through changes in membrane permeability [Enr-3]. Nevertheless the changes are permanent, and this also points out in favor of the hypothesis that D_2O concentration acts as a parameter rather than a state variable.

Thus no matter what is the nature of the mechanism of the detereum effects on the circadian oscillator, the dynamic behavior is the same. The distinction between linear effects, as in Enright's experiments, versus the nonlinear effects, in the Bruce and Pittendrigh experiments, is probably quantitative rather than qualitative. There are many examples of nonlinear oscillators where the period is rarely a linear function of the parameters of the differential equation. The "adaptation" may have to do more with the overall physiology of the organism than with the circadian regulator.

The difference in the mode of action between temperature and heavy water is not surprising. Variations in the former are quite frequent in the natural environment, and they would have helped select in favor of a compensating mechanism. Variations in the latter are rare, if at all, under natural conditions, and thus it is less likely for compensating mechanisms to be selected for. In terms of model building, compensated environmental factors act as state variables while uncompensated ones as parameters.

An interesting possibility is that heavy water acts by affecting the coupling among a population of oscillatory units which constitute that regulator. In Section 8.3 we describe a system of interacting biochemical oscillators where the coupling occurs, possibly, through the interstitial fluid. The presence of heavy water would have a definite effect there. Since the frequency of oscillations depends strongly on the mutual coupling strength (see Sections 7.5, 8.2, and 8.3), it will also be affected by the concentration of D_2O.

6.6   Bibliographical Notes

Efforts to modify the behavior of biological oscillators by external agents have a long history. However the results have been rather negative. Certain agents have a direct effect, which is expected from the function of the system (e.g., light in circadian oscillators). In general the response of the oscillator to such agents is exactly the one predicted from the functional significance of the system, and one does not obtain any insight into its structure [Pav-10]. Other agents have very drastic effects throughout the organism, and it is difficult if not impossible to distinguish any specific effects on the oscillator. This has been particularly true with chemical agents in the case of circadian clocks [Has-1, Has-2, Has-3, Kar-1, Kar-2, Swe-3, Swe-4, Van-1, Van-2, Van-3]. The more interesting are those agents which have a graduated effect on the oscillation. Temperature is one of them. It is not surprising that circadian oscillators present temperature compensation but the form of compensation is significant for understanding the structure of the oscillator. Cyclohexamide [Fel-1], heavy water [Enr-3], and ethyl alcohol [Enr-4] are three agents which seem to act as parameters (see Sections 6.4 and 6.5). Oscillations in cultures of fungi are quite susceptible to chemical manipulation [Jer-1], and their study may eventually provide more insight into the nature of biological oscillators than those of more complex organisms. Other agents can be used to obtain PRC's [Esk-4, Hal-5].

Surgical lesions have been tried in many cases [Bra-1, Bra-2, Bra-3, Nis-1, Nis-2, Nis-3, Rob-3, Rob-4, Rob-5]. In general they provide more evidence about the peripheral components of the system than the main oscillator. The situation is further complicated by the number of ways by which the organism perceives its environment. Nonoptical light perception is one example [Adl-1, Adl-2, Bin-1, Gas-1, Gas-2, Men-2, Men-4].

The distinction between "permanent" and "temporary" graduated changes may be more helpful in the search for the biological clock, if it is coupled with a model for the mechanism involved.

CHAPTER 7

Populations of Interacting Oscillators

7.1 Introduction

There is little need to emphasize the importance of this subject for the study of biological systems. Not only is there experimental evidence that many biological clocks do indeed consist of a group of interacting oscillators but also one can expect *a priori* that the usual anatomical redundancy will manifest itself in more than one time-keeping component for any given function.

Unfortunately the mathematical literature on the subject is very limited, and for good reason. The study of high-order nonlinear systems is a hard subject in itself. The case of oscillatory high-order systems presents additional difficulties; namely, that the application of linearization techniques is not always meaningful because of the structural instability of such systems. Thus a purely mathematical analysis cannot say much about the behavior of populations of interacting oscillators.

Quite often nonlinear systems are studied through computer simulation (analog or digital). This requires the choice of specific values of parameters. However the behavior of complex systems depends strongly on the choice of these values* and one is faced with a virtually insurmountable task again.

A combination of mathematical analysis and simulation seems fruitful. The limited results of the former can serve as a guide for the latter, and also they give some indications about the general validity of the conclusions of specific simulations.

---

* Sometimes one reads the opposite statement in the literature. The two are not really contradictory. Small changes of parameters are indeed less significant in a complex system than in a simple one. However, the opposite is true for large changes. See Section 7 for more on this subject.

In the sequence we will discuss first the subject of structural stability and show the limitations of the analytical techniques. A brief description of them will be next, followed by the study of synchronization of populations of oscillators. Finally, a discussion of the main features of populations as distinct from single oscillators will be given.

7.2 Structural Stability

As we mentioned in the first chapter, there are no general mathematical techniques for the study of high-order nonlinear systems, except for the ones based on their approximation by linear systems. Thus populations of interacting oscillators can only be studied in this way, if at all. Unfortunately, in many cases even these techniques are not applicable. In order to see the reason for this difficulty we must first discuss the concept of *structural stability* [And-I, Bog-I].

Consider the following (nth-order) nonlinear system:

$$d\mathbf{x}/dt = \mathbf{f}(\mathbf{x}) \qquad (7.2.1)$$

Let $\mathbf{x}(t; \mathbf{x}_0, t_0)$ be its state at time t when at time t_0 its state was $\mathbf{x}_0$. Let $\tilde{\mathbf{x}}(t; \tilde{\mathbf{x}}_0, t_0)$ be the similar quantity for the following system:

$$d\mathbf{x}/dt = \mathbf{f}(\mathbf{x}) + \mathbf{g}(\mathbf{x}) \qquad (7.2.2)$$

Now let t vary within a finite interval of time (t_1, t_2). Then a well-known result from the theory of differential equations states that the difference between the two vectors will be small if the difference in the initial states and the "perturbation" $\mathbf{g}(\mathbf{x})$ were small. Formally we have that for a given $\delta > 0$ the norm

$$\| \mathbf{x}(t; \mathbf{x}_0, t_0) - \tilde{\mathbf{x}}(t; \tilde{\mathbf{x}}_0, t_0)\| \qquad \text{for} \quad t_1 \leqslant t \leqslant t_2$$

can be made less than δ provided that

$$\| \mathbf{x}_0 - \tilde{\mathbf{x}}_0 \| \qquad \text{and} \qquad \| \mathbf{g}(\mathbf{x})\|$$

are less than some constant $\varepsilon > 0$. This property is known as the continuity of the solutions of differential equations over a finite interval of time.

However this result does not hold in general for an infinite interval of time, which is the really interesting case in the approximate analysis of systems. One wants to know that the trajectories of the approximate systems are close to the trajectories of the original system at all times and not just over a finite interval. Systems whose trajectories satisfy this property over an infinite interval of time are called *structurally stable*. The following is a formal definition.

DEFINITION 7.2.1. The system of Eq. (7.2.1) will be called structurally stable if for any $\varepsilon > 0$ there is a $\delta > 0$ such that, if

$$\| \mathbf{g}(\mathbf{x})\| = \delta$$

then there is a topological transformation of the state space into itself, for which each trajectory is mapped into a trajectory of the system described by Eq. (7.2.2) and the points corresponding to each other are at a distance less than ε; i.e.,

$$\| \mathbf{x}(t; \mathbf{x}_0 , t_0) - \tilde{\mathbf{x}}(t; \tilde{\mathbf{x}}_0 , t_0)\| < \varepsilon$$

EXAMPLE 7.2.1.   Consider the harmonic oscillator

$$dx_1/dt = x_2 \tag{7.2.3a}$$

$$dx_2/dt = -x_1 \tag{7.2.3b}$$

Its trajectories are closed circles with center at $(0, 0)$. Now let $\mathbf{g}(\mathbf{x})$ be given by

$$g_1(x_1 , x_2) = ux_1 \tag{7.2.4a}$$

$$g_2(x_1 , x_2) = 0 \tag{7.2.4b}$$

The new system has damped oscillations with a damping coefficient $u/2$ (if $u > 0$) or increasing oscillations (if $u < 0$). Although it is possible to find a finite interval over which the damped oscillations do not differ much from the sustained oscillations, it is not possible to do so for an infinite interval no matter how small u is. Thus the system of Eqs. (7.2.3) is not structurally stable.

EXAMPLE 7.2.2.   Consider the following linear system:

$$d\mathbf{x}/dt = \mathbf{A}\mathbf{x} \tag{7.2.5}$$

The behavior of its trajectories depends only on the eigenvalues of $\mathbf{A}$, and any change which does not affect the sign of their real parts or makes an imaginary part zero or creates a complex eigenvalue from a real one is going to leave the new trajectories close to the old ones. Since it is true that the eigenvalues of a matrix are continuous functions of its elements, the system of Eq. (7.2.5) will be structurally stable if all the eigenvalues of **A** have real and imaginary parts different than zero. This holds true even if the change in the system is nonlinear.

The above examples indicate that a linear conservative system cannot be structurally stable. It can be shown that:

THEOREM 7.2.1. If a nonlinear system S has a singularity in whose neighborhood can be approximated by a linear conservative system, then S is not structurally stable.

THEOREM 7.2.2. A conservative system (linear or nonlinear) is not structurally stable.

Proofs of these theorems and extensive discussions of the topic of structural stability can be found in the mathematical literature [And-I, Bog-I].

These results indicate that setting $\varepsilon = 0$ is an equation of the form

$$dx/dt = \mathbf{A}x + \varepsilon F(\mathbf{x}) \qquad (7.2.6)$$

and assuming that the resulting linear system has trajectories which are close to those of the original system is not justified if **A** has only imaginary eigenvalues. Since the latter is usually the case with nonlinear oscillators, such approximations are not valid in their case. However, something can be salvaged.

We described in the first chapter an approximate analysis of the system

$$d^2x/dt_2 + \varepsilon f(x)\, dx/dt + \omega^2 x = 0 \qquad (7.2.7)$$

This was made possible by concentrating our attention on one single trajectory of the form

$$x(t) = a(t)\cos(\omega t + \theta) \qquad (7.2.8)$$

where the time derivatives of both a and θ could have been made arbitrarily small for sufficiently small ε. Then we were able to derive conditions for the average values of $a(t)$ and $\theta(t)$ so that they were close to a trajectory of the system (7.2.7). In this analysis we were concerned with the proximity (over an infinite interval of time) of only a *single* trajectory (the limit cycle) of the original system to the corresponding one of the linearized system. A similar method can be applied for a high-order system. This would check the possibility of a *monofrequency oscillation*. However, in contrast to Eq. (7.2.7), the linearizations of such systems have usually more than one characteristic frequency, and therefore a number of difficulties arise. The main one is related to the study of multifrequency oscillations. Because of the nonlinear nature of the system these cannot be derived as superpositions of monofrequency oscillations. A second difficulty is that we do not have any general analytical tests for the stability of even the monofrequency oscillations. We will describe these methods in the next section, and then we will illustrate these points with some examples.

7.3   Monofrequency Oscillations in Systems of Coupled Oscillators Studied by Asymptotic Techniques

The method of Krylov–Bogoliubov–Mitropolsky [Bog-I] discussed in the first chapter can be extended to the study of coupled oscillators. The following equation describes such a system:

$$d^2\mathbf{x}/dt^2 - \varepsilon\mathbf{f}(\mathbf{x}, d\mathbf{x}/dt) + \mathbf{A}\mathbf{x} = 0 \tag{7.3.1}$$

This assumes not only linear "elastic" coupling but possibly nonlinear "fricational" coupling as well. For $\varepsilon = 0$ the linearized system has a general solution of the form

$$\mathbf{x}(t) = \sum_{i=1}^{n} a_i \mathbf{y}_i \cos(\omega_1 t + \theta_i) \tag{7.3.2}$$

where a_i and θ_i are constants determined from the initial conditions, $\mathbf{y}_i$ $(i = 1, 2,..., n)$ are normalized eigenvectors of $\mathbf{A}$, and ω_i $(i = 1, 2,..., n)$ are square roots of the eigenvalues of $\mathbf{A}$. The formalism in Eq. (7.3.2) assumes that all eigenvalues of $\mathbf{A}$ are positive. We will keep this assumption in the sequence.

In a manner similar to the one discussed in the first chapter, we will try for a solution of (7.3.1) of the form

$$\mathbf{x}(t) = a(t)\mathbf{y} \cos \Psi \tag{7.3.3}$$

where $\Psi = \omega t + \theta(t)$, ω^2 is an eigenvalue of $\mathbf{A}$, and $\mathbf{y}$ is an eigenvector of $\mathbf{A}$ ($\| \mathbf{y} \| = 1$). We also assume that there exist functions $A_1(a)$ and $B_1(a)$ such that

$$da/dt = \varepsilon A_1(a) \tag{7.3.4}$$

$$d\theta/dt = \varepsilon B_1(a) \tag{7.3.5}$$

Differentiating Eq. (7.3.3) by taking into account (7.3.4) and (7.3.5) and ignoring terms which are multiplied by ε^2 results in

$$d^2\mathbf{x}/dt^2 + \mathbf{A}\mathbf{x} = -2\varepsilon\omega\mathbf{y}(A_1 \sin \Psi + aB_1 \cos \Psi) \tag{7.3.6}$$

Substituting Eq. (7.3.6) into (7.3.1) yields

$$-\mathbf{f}(\mathbf{x}, d\mathbf{x}/dt) - 2\omega\mathbf{y}(A_1 \sin \Psi + aB_1 \cos \Psi) = 0 \qquad (7.3.7)$$

Taking the scalar product of both sides of Eq. (7.3.7) with $\mathbf{y}$ we obtain

$$A_1 \sin \Psi + aB_1 \cos \Psi = -(1/2\omega)\langle\mathbf{f}(\mathbf{x}, d\mathbf{x}/dt), \mathbf{y}\rangle \qquad (7.3.8)$$

or, in an explicit form,

$$A_1 \sin \Psi + aB_1 \cos \Psi = -\frac{1}{2\omega} \sum_{k=1}^{n} y_k f_k(a\mathbf{y} \cos \Psi, -a\mathbf{y}\omega \sin \Psi) \qquad (7.3.9)$$

If the right-hand side of the above equation is expanded in a Fourier series, then obviously A_1 will equal the coefficient of $\sin \Psi$ term and aB_1 will equal the coefficient of the $\cos \Psi$ term. Thus we have

$$A_1(a) = -\frac{1}{2\pi\omega} \int_0^{2\pi} \sum_{k=1}^{n} y_k f_k(a\mathbf{y} \cos \Psi, -a\mathbf{y}\omega \sin \Psi) \sin \Psi \, d\Psi \qquad (7.3.10)$$

$$B_1(a) = -\frac{1}{2\pi\omega a} \int_0^{2\pi} \sum_{k=1}^{n} y_k f_k(a\mathbf{y} \cos \Psi, -a\mathbf{y}\omega \sin \Psi) \cos \Psi \, d\Psi \qquad (7.3.11)$$

Note the resemblance of these equations and (1.5.13) and (1.5.14). The above equations can be put into Eqs. (7.3.4) and (7.3.5) and then the latter can be solved to obtain explicit expressions for $a(t)$ and $\theta(t)$.

This analysis indicates the following properties about oscillations of the system (7.3.1):

(i) The square roots of the eigenvalues of $\mathbf{A}$ correspond to frequencies of oscillations which can occur in the system.

(ii) The eigenvectors of $\mathbf{A}$ multiplied by an appropriate time function correspond to solutions of the system.

The form of $A_1(a)$ can give some information about the local stability of the solution given by Eq. (7.3.3). However, the above analysis provides no information about the region of attraction of a solution nor does it say anything about multifrequency oscillations.

Some further insight may be gained by studying a specific example:

EXAMPLE 7.3.1. We consider a group of coupled van der Pol oscillators where

$$f_i\left(\mathbf{x}, \frac{d\mathbf{x}}{dt}\right) = \left[1 - \left(\sum_{j=1}^{n} b_{ij}x_j\right)^2\right] \frac{dx_i}{dt} \qquad (7.3.12)$$

i.e., there exists frictional coupling.

Substituting Eq. (7.3.3) and its derivative into (7.3.12) we obtain

$$f_i\left(\mathbf{x}, \frac{d\mathbf{x}}{dt}\right) = -a y_i \omega \sin \Psi + a^3 y_i \omega \sin \Psi \cos^2 \Psi \left(\sum_{j=1}^{n} b_{ij} y_i\right)^2 \quad (7.3.13)$$

Therefore we have

$$A_1(a) = \frac{a}{2\pi}\left[\sum_{i=1}^{n} y_i{}^2\right]\int_0^{2\pi} \sin^2 \Psi \, d\Psi$$

$$- \frac{a^3}{2\pi}\left[\sum_{i=1}^{n} y_i{}^2 \left(\sum_{j=1}^{n} b_{ij} y_j\right)^2\right]\int_0^{2\pi} \sin^2 \Psi \cos^2 \Psi \, d\Psi$$

or (because $\|\mathbf{y}\| = 1$)

$$A_1(a) = \frac{a}{2}\left\{1 - \frac{a^2}{4}\left[\sum_{i=1}^{n} y_i{}^2 \left(\sum_{j=1}^{n} b_{ij} y_j\right)^2\right]\right\} \quad (7.3.14)$$

It is easy to verify that the integrals in the right-hand side of the expression for $B_1(a)$ are both zero and therefore

$$B_1(a) = 0 \quad (7.3.15)$$

Thus the phase of the oscillations is constant, at least within terms of ε^2. Equation (7.3.14) is quite similar to the one obtained for a single oscillator and implies the existence of an oscillation of amplitude

$$a_0 = \frac{2}{[\sum_{i=1}^{n} y_i{}^2(\sum_{j=1}^{n} b_{ij} y_j)^2]^{1/2}} \quad (7.3.16)$$

One might say that this is a locally stable oscillation on the basis of the same reasoning as in Section 1.5. However, this is not true here. A perturbation of the solution

$$a_0 \cos \Psi$$

will not involve not only changes in the amplitude a_0 but also the introduction of other frequencies (the latter possibility did not exist in the case of one oscillator).

Let us now consider an even more special case, namely the presence of only frictional coupling. Then $\mathbf{A}$ will be a diagonal matrix with elements

$$a_{kk} = \omega_k{}^2$$

The eigenvectors $\mathbf{y}$ will have all their components zero except one, which will be equal to 1. Then Eq. (7.3.3) reduces to

$$x_i(t) = 0 \quad \text{if} \quad i \neq k$$
$$x_k(t) = a(t) \cos(\omega_k t + \theta_0) \tag{7.3.17}$$

This is obviously an unrealistic result, since it describes only one oscillator with nonzero output and all others with zero output, in spite of the frictional coupling and the instability of the $(0, 0)$ state for a van der Pol oscillator. The reason for this obviously wrong conclusion is the fact that the above analysis ignores the interaction of very small terms (the ones depending on ε), which in this special case are the only ones providing coupling. The only positive conclusion we can make is that, *because of the weak coupling, monofrequency oscillations are not possible.*

Another special case is provided when there is only elastic coupling. The absence of frictional coupling implies that b_{ij} is zero if $i \neq j$ and we can take it equal to 1 if $i = j$. Then Eq. (7.3.16) becomes

$$a_0 = \frac{2}{\left(\sum_{i=1}^{n} y_i^4\right)^{1/2}} \tag{7.3.18}$$

In subsequent sections we will give examples of a matrix $\mathbf{A}$ with eigenvectors of the following form: $\mathbf{y}^1$ has all its components equal to $1/\sqrt{n}$; $\mathbf{y}^2, ..., \mathbf{y}^n$ are characterized by the fact that the sum of their components is zero.

If ω_1^2 is the eigenvalue of $\mathbf{A}$ corresponding to $\mathbf{y}^1$ Eq. (7.3.3) becomes

$$x_i(t) = [a(t)/\sqrt{n}] \cos(\omega_1 t + \theta_0) \tag{7.3.19a}$$

i.e., all units oscillate in synchrony and in phase.

Equation (7.3.18) yields

$$a_0 = 2\sqrt{n}$$

and, replacing into Eq. (7.3.19a), we obtain

$$x_i(t) \approx 2 \cos(\omega_1 t + \theta_0) \tag{7.3.19b}$$

i.e., the amplitude of each oscillator is the same as though it were oscillating without coupling.

A similar result is obtained (for n even) if we consider an eigenvector of the following form:

$$\mathbf{y}^2 = \underbrace{(1/\sqrt{n}, ..., 1/\sqrt{n}}_{n/2 \text{ terms}}, \underbrace{-1/\sqrt{n}, ..., -1/\sqrt{n})}_{n/2 \text{ terms}} \tag{7.3.20}$$

Replacing (7.3.20) into (7.3.18) and then into (7.3.3) yields

$$x_i(t) = 2\cos(\omega_2 t + \theta_0), \qquad i = 1, 2, ..., n/2$$
$$x_i(t) = -2\cos(\omega_2 t + \theta_0), \qquad i = n/2 + 1, n/2 + 2, ..., n \qquad (7.3.21)$$

In this case the oscillators form two groups with opposite phases. Finally let us consider a third eigenvector,

$$\mathbf{y}^3 = (n - 1)^{1/2}/n, -1/[n(n - 1)]^{1/2}, ..., -1/[n(n - 1)]^{1/2} \qquad (7.3.22)$$

Then Eq. (7.3.18) yields

$$a_0 = \frac{2n}{[(n - 1)^3 + 1]^{1/2}/(n - 1)} \qquad (7.3.23)$$

and Eq. (7.3.3) results in

$$x_1(t) = \frac{2(n - 1)\sqrt{n}}{[(n - 1)^3 + 1]^{1/2}} \cos(\omega_3 t + \theta_0)$$

$$x_i(t) = -\frac{2\sqrt{n}}{[(n - 1)^3 + 1]^{1/2}} \cos(\omega_3 t + \theta_0), \qquad i = 2, ..., n \qquad (7.3.24)$$

One oscillator has considerably greater amplitude $(n - 1$ times) than the others and opposite phase to the rest of them.

All three monofrequency oscillations just described seem feasible. One might assume that, depending on the initial conditions, a different one might be reached in steady state. However, there is no mathematical justification for such a conclusion. We do not even know whether they are stable. To study even local stability it will be necessary to consider perturbations of Eq. (7.3.3) in terms of the vector $\mathbf{y}$; i.e., combinations of solutions of the type discussed above, and we simply do not have the analytical tools for that.

7.4 Strategies for the Study of Populations of Oscillators

The discussion of the previous two sections has shown the difficulties of a purely analytical approach. It seems thus important to establish a mixed strategy involving both analysis and computer simulation. This can be summarized as follows.

(i) Given a system S of interacting oscillators, obtain its linear approximation and determine the eigenvectors and eigenvalues of the latter. Let them be denoted by $(\omega_i^2, \mathbf{y}_i)$ $(i = 1, 2,..., n)$. If there exist negative eigenvalues, then the possibility of global instability of the system exists.

(ii)   For each $i = 1, 2,..., n$, obtain the conditions for monofrequency oscillations using the technique of Section 7.3 (or one similar to it). If these conditions are satisfied, then one has a possible solution but no information about its stability or region of attraction. Some solutions can be rejected outright on the basis of physical reasoning [as in Eq. (7.3.18) of the previous section], but one should be very careful in using such arguments.

(iii)   Check on the computer the local stability of the monofrequency oscillations. Use as initial conditions values of $\mathbf{x}$ equal to $a_0\mathbf{y}$ and check whether $\mathbf{x}(t)$ converges to a periodic solution of the corresponding frequency.

(iv)   Check on the computer the existence of stable multifrequency oscillators. Use as initial conditions values of $\mathbf{x}$ which are different to any of the $a_0\mathbf{y}$'s corresponding to stable monofrequency oscillations. This is the most difficult part of the study and, strictly speaking, one is usually not sure whether certain multifrequency oscillations do not exist, even if they never are observed during the simulation. The possibility remains that some solution with a "small" region of attraction has been missed.

In general multifrequency oscillations will be almost periodic rather than periodic unless the eigenvalues of $\mathbf{A}$ have rational ratios.

7.5   Synchronization of Populations of Oscillators: The Weakly Nonlinear Case

Although monofrequency oscillations may have a limited mathematical interest, they seem to be quite important from a biological viewpoint. It is only then that a population of oscillators can operate as a biological clock. The state when all units oscillate at the same frequency is often referred to as mutual synchronization. The discussion of Section 7.3 has shown that the frequencies where synchronization is possible are square roots of the eigenvalues of the coupling matrix $\mathbf{A}$. The following discussion will help us gain some insight into the nature of mutual synchronization.

First we must clarify certain aspects of the discussion of Section 7.3. The study of monofrequency oscillations there assumes that all oscillators either are in phase or have a $180°$ phase difference. However, in principle it is possible to have units with different phases so that Eq. (7.3.3) will be of the form

$$x_i(t) = a(t) y_i \cos[\omega t + \theta_i(t)], \qquad i = 1, 2,..., n \qquad (7.5.1)$$

We will now use a different method to study this case. Equation (7.3.1) can be rewritten as follows:

$$d^2\mathbf{x}/dt^2 - \varepsilon\mathbf{f}(\mathbf{x}, d\mathbf{x}/dt) + \omega^2\mathbf{x} = (\omega^2\mathbf{I} - \mathbf{A})\mathbf{x} \qquad (7.5.2)$$

where ω^2 is an eigenvalue of $\mathbf{A}$. Suppose now for simplicity that there is no frictional coupling and also $\mathbf{f}$ is of such form as to have

$$B_1(a) = 0$$

Then

$$\theta_i(t) = \theta_i \qquad (7.5.3)$$

and the right-hand side of Eq. (7.5.2) will be of the form

$$a(t)\left[\omega^2 y_k \cos(\omega t + \theta_k) - \sum_{j=1}^{n} a_{kj} y_j \cos(\omega t + \theta_j)\right] \qquad (7.5.4)$$

It is easy to verify that the quantity within the brackets can be written in the form of

$$C_k \cos(\omega t + \theta_k') \qquad (7.5.5)$$

for properly chosen C_k and θ_k' and that in general $\theta_k' \neq \theta_k$.

Thus Eq. (7.5.2) will describe now oscillators which are subject to an input of the same frequency but different phase. We have seen in Chapter 4 that this is a likely occurrence in entrainment, and therefore monofrequency solutions of the form described by Eq. (7.5.1) are possible.

In order to illustrate the analysis of synchronization we consider a system of the kind described by Eq. (7.3.1) where the elements a_{kj} of $\mathbf{A}$ are given by the following relations [Pav-8]:

$$\text{If} \quad k \neq j, \quad a_{kj} = r\omega^2 \qquad (7.5.6)$$

$$\text{If} \quad k = j, \quad a_{kk} = \omega^2 \qquad (7.5.7)$$

Thus there is elastic coupling where each oscillator affects uniformly all the others.

The eigenvalues of $\mathbf{A}$ are given by the following equation:

$$\det |\mathbf{A} - \lambda\mathbf{I}| = \det \begin{vmatrix} \omega^2 - \lambda & r\omega^2 & \cdots & r\omega^2 \\ r\omega^2 & \omega^2 - \lambda & \cdots & r\omega^2 \\ r\omega^2 & & \cdots & \omega^2 - \lambda \end{vmatrix} = 0 \qquad (7.5.8)$$

Equation (7.5.8) can be transformed by factoring out $r\omega^2$ and defining a new variable

$$x = (\omega^2 - \lambda)/r\omega^2 \qquad (7.5.9)$$

Then it becomes

$$\det \begin{vmatrix} x & 1 & \cdots & 1 \\ 1 & x & \cdots & 1 \\ 1 & 1 & \cdots & x \end{vmatrix} = 0 \qquad (7.5.10)$$

One can verify* that Eq. (7.5.11) has a simple root

$$x_1 = -(n - 1) \qquad (7.5.11)$$

and a multiple root

$$x_2 = x_3 = \cdots = x_n = 1 \qquad (7.5.12)$$

Thus the eigenvalues of **A** are

$$\lambda_1 = \omega^2[1 + r(n - 1)] \qquad \text{with multiplicity} \quad 1 \qquad (7.5.13)$$

and

$$\lambda_2 = \omega^2[1 - r] \qquad \text{with multiplicity} \quad n - 1 \qquad (7.5.14)$$

The eigenvector corresponding to λ_1 is

$$\mathbf{y}_1 = (y, y, \ldots, y) \qquad (7.5.15)$$

where y is any number.

There are $n - 1$ linearly independent eigenvectors corresponding to λ_2 and they are defined by

$$\sum_{i=1}^{n} y_i{}^m = 0, \qquad m = 2, \ldots, n - 1 \qquad (7.5.16)$$

These were used in the example of Section 7.3. Because the analysis of that section required orthonormal eigenvectors y was taken to equal $1/\sqrt{n}$. Those results pointed out only possible monofrequency oscillations but they said nothing about their stability. We will attempt to answer the latter question now.

First we notice that in a monofrequency oscillation at

$$\omega_1 = \sqrt{\lambda_1} = \omega[1 + r(n - 1)]^{1/2} \qquad (7.5.17)$$

---

* By adding all the rows to the first one, factoring out the term $x + n - 1$, and then subtracting the first row from all the rest.

the sum of all the variables x_1, x_2,..., x_n is simply

$$S(t) = nx_i(t) \tag{7.5.18}$$

If the oscillation is at

$$\omega_2 = \sqrt{\lambda_2} = \omega(1 - r)^{1/2} \tag{7.5.19}$$

then, because of Eq. (7.5.16), the sum is identically zero.

We will use now a special technique to study their stability for the case when the nonlinear term is given by

$$f_i(\mathbf{x}, d\mathbf{x}/dt) = g(x_i) \, dx_i/dt, \qquad i = 1, 2,..., n \tag{7.5.20}$$

where g is an even function of its argument and twice differentiable.

Suppose now that the state of the system is in the neighborhood of a solution corresponding to ω_1, namely

$$x_i = x + \delta_i \tag{7.5.21}$$

Substituting in (7.5.20) and using a Taylor expansion we obtain

$$f_i(\mathbf{x}, d\mathbf{x}/dt) = [g(x) + \delta_i g'(x)] \, dx_i/dt \tag{7.5.22}$$

Let us now add term by term all the scalar equations of Eq. (7.3.1) for the present form of $\mathbf{A}$. For sufficiently small δ_i the terms which are multiplied by $\varepsilon\delta_i$ can be ignored. Thus we obtain the following equation for the sum

$$d^2s/dt^2 - \varepsilon g(s/n) \, ds/dt + \omega^2[1 + r(n - 1)]s = 0 \tag{7.5.23}$$

This has the same functional form as the equation for a single uncoupled oscillator, and thus in general will have a *stable* limit cycle where the oscillation will have a frequency equal to ω_1 and its amplitude will be about n times the one of the uncoupled oscillation. These agree with the characteristics of the first solution, and therefore we can conclude that this is indeed a stable solution, at least locally.

We consider next a solution corresponding to ω_2 and in particular one of the forms given by Eq. (7.3.20). Let

$$x_i(t) = x(t) + \delta_i \qquad \text{if} \quad i \leqslant n/2$$
$$x_i(t) = -x(t) + \delta_i \qquad \text{if} \quad i > n/2 \tag{7.5.24}$$

where

$$x(t) = 2\cos(\omega_2 t) \tag{7.5.25}$$

Summing up the scalar equations of Eq. (7.3.1) we obtain for the sum s the following equation:

$$d^2s/dt^2 - \varepsilon g(x)\, ds/dt + \omega^2[1 + r(n-1)]s = 0 \qquad (7.5.26)$$

or

$$d^2s/dt^2 - \varepsilon f(2\cos\omega_2 t)\, ds/dt + \omega_1{}^2 s = 0 \qquad (7.5.27)$$

If ω_2 is significantly greater than ω_1, then one may assume that considering the time average of the nonlinear term will give a good approximation to the solution. This is actually justified in general because the time-varying term is multiplied by a "small" constant ε. Thus Eq. (7.5.27) may be approximated by

$$\frac{d^2s}{dt^2} - \frac{\varepsilon\omega_2}{2\pi}\left[\int_0^{2\pi/\omega_2} g(2\cos\omega_2 t)\, dt\right]\frac{ds}{dt} + \omega_1{}^2 s = 0 \qquad (7.5.28)$$

In the case of the van der Pol oscillator,

$$g(x) = 1 - x^2 \qquad (7.5.29)$$

and hence the term in brackets equals

$$\int_0^{2\pi/\omega_2} (1 - 4\cos^2\omega_2 t)\, dt = -\frac{2\pi}{\omega_2} \qquad (7.5.30)$$

Then Eq. (7.5.28) takes the form

$$d^2s/dt^2 + \varepsilon\, ds/dt + \omega_1{}^2 s = 0 \qquad (7.5.31)$$

which has a stable solution $s \to 0$ as $t \to \infty$.

Therefore, the solution of the form given by Eq. (7.3.20) is stable locally.

We conclude that a system of coupled oscillators can have more than one locally stable solutions.

Since this example dealt with identical and symmetrically coupled oscillators the practical validity of its results may be questioned. It turns out that they are valid even if the oscillators are not identical and the coupling not symmetrical. This is so because the eigenvalues are continuous functions of the elements of a matrix. Table 7.5.1 illustrates this. $\mathbf{A}$ was first taken to be as given by Eq. (7.5.6) and (7.5.7) with $\omega^2 = 1$ and $n = 20$. Then, for various values of r, a number of perturbed matrices were generated by adding to the diagonal elements a random element uniformly distributed between $-x$ and x while the other elements were set equal to

$$(r + z)\,\omega_a{}^2$$

TABLE 7.5.1

EFFECT OF DIFFERENCES AMONG INDIVIDUAL UNITS ON THE EIGENVALUES OF THE COUPLING
MATRIX

			Eigenvalues		
r	x	y	λ_1	$\max(\lambda_2, ..., \lambda_n)$	$\min(\lambda_2, ..., \lambda_n)$
0.05	0.00	0.000	1.950	0.950	0.950
0.05	0.00	0.005	1.948	0.970	0.929
0.05	0.00	0.010	1.960	0.990	0.906
0.05	0.00	0.015	1.946	1.010	0.873
0.05	0.15	0.000	1.901	1.071	0.806
0.05	0.15	0.005	1.933	1.077	0.805
0.05	0.15	0.010	1.979	1.112	0.814
0.05	0.15	0.015	2.002	1.116	0.783
0.15	0.00	0.000	3.850	0.850	0.850
0.15	0.00	0.015	3.865	0.920	0.767
0.15	0.00	0.030	3.901	0.988	0.720
0.15	0.00	0.045	3.880	1.074	0.628
0.15	0.15	0.000	3.892	0.978	0.731
0.15	0.15	0.015	3.856	0.990	0.709
0.15	0.15	0.030	3.891	1.040	0.647
0.15	0.15	0.045	3.813	1.088	0.600

where ω_a^2 was the numerical mean of the diagonal elements and z
a random variable uniformly distributed between $-y$ and y. Note that,
for the maximum values of x and y used, the diagonal elements varied
by $\pm 15\%$ while the other elements varied by $\pm 30\%$.

It is also true that, if the eigenvectors of a matrix form a basis for the
corresponding vector space, then they are also continuous functions of
its coefficients. This is clearly the case in the present example. Table 7.5.2
shows the results for the matrices used in Table 7.5.1. Since it is not
easy to plot twenty-dimensional vectors, we have used instead some
functions of their components to illustrate the continuity.

7.6　Synchronization of Populations of Oscillators: The General Case

All the previous sections have dealt with weakly nonlinear oscillators.
Here we will study a system without this constraint. The following

TABLE 7.5.2

EFFECT OF DIFFERENCES AMONG INDIVIDUAL UNITS ON THE
EIGENVECTORS OF THE COUPLING MATRIX

			Eigenvectors			
r	x	y	$\max_i y_i^1$	$\min_i y_i^1$	$\sum_{i=1}^n y_i^1$	$\max_{j=2,\ldots,n} \mid \sum_{i=1}^n y_i^j \mid$
0.05	0.00	0.000	$0.224 = 1/(20)^{1/2}$	0.224	4.472	0.000
0.05	0.00	0.005	0.233	0.211	4.471	0.030
0.05	0.00	0.010	0.241	0.200	4.465	0.108
0.05	0.00	0.015	0.237	0.199	4.467	0.095
0.05	0.15	0.000	0.262	0.197	4.452	0.339
0.05	0.15	0.005	0.267	0.191	4.451	0.233
0.05	0.15	0.010	0.269	0.182	4.450	0.285
0.05	0.15	0.015	0.260	0.171	4.437	0.275
0.15	0.00	0.000	$0.224 = 1/(20)^{1/2}$	0.224	4.472	0.000
0.15	0.00	0.015	0.233	0.213	4.471	0.037
0.15	0.00	0.030	0.244	0.209	4.468	0.087
0.15	0.00	0.045	0.254	0.192	4.459	0.182
0.15	0.15	0.000	0.233	0.214	4.471	0.069
0.15	0.15	0.015	0.240	0.214	4.470	0.076
0.15	0.15	0.030	0.242	0.203	4.468	0.116
0.15	0.15	0.045	0.253	0.197	4.463	0.109

equations describe a large class of populations of interacting oscillators [Pav-11]:

$$dx_k/dt = f_k(x_k, y_k, z_k), \qquad k = 1, 2, \ldots, n \qquad (7.6.1)$$

$$dy_k/dt = g_k(x_k, y_k, z_k) \qquad k = 1, 2, \ldots, n \qquad (7.6.2)$$

$$z_k = \mathscr{F}\left(\sum_{j=1}^n a_{kj} x_j\right), \qquad k = 1, 2, \ldots, n \qquad (7.6.3)$$

$\mathscr{F}$ is a dynamic operator with the property that, if its argument is a periodic function, the same will be true for z_k and its period will be the same as the period of the argument. This condition is satisfied for delay operators, simple nonlinearities, nonlinearities with hysteresis, the inverse of linear differential equations (i.e., if x_k satisfies such an equation whose input is the argument of $\mathscr{F}$), and superpositions of such operators. Practically speaking, we allow $\mathscr{F}$ to be anything else except a nonlinear differential equation.

Let us consider for the moment only Eqs. (7.6.1) and (7.6.2) with z_k as an external input. A *synchronous solution*, i.e., one where all the x_k's and y_k's oscillate with the same period T, can be achieved only if z_k

entrains the corresponding oscillator to that period. (Another possibility is that each unit has a natural oscillation with period T and z_k fails to disturb it. Obviously this has no practical interest.)

The entrainment of each unit can be harmonic (z_k has itself period T), subharmonic (z_k has a period which is an integer multiple of T, mT), or superharmonic (z_k has a period which is an integer fraction of T, T/m). Because of our assumption about $\mathscr{F}$ the sums $\sum_{j=1}^{n} a_{kj}x_i$ will have the corresponding periods. This imposes the condition for achieving synchronous solutions. We examine various special cases:

(i)   All the units are in phase. Then, if $a_{kj} > 0$, all the sums will oscillate at that period and a synchronous solution can exist if the individual oscillators are entrainable by z_k to a common period. This usually means that the mutual coupling should be strong enough.

(ii)   The units form two groups with half a period phase difference. Then the sums will oscillate with a fundamental period equal to $T/2$, and a synchronous solution can exist only if z_k can cause subharmonic entrainment of the individual units.

(iii)   The previous case can be generalized by assuming that the units form m groups which have phase difference T/m and they are entrained by z_k to m times their period.

Each of these possibilities will be called an *mth-order synchronization*, where m is the number of groups which the oscillators are split into.

Note that the units need not actually be in phase but small phase differences are allowed as long as the sums $\sum_{j=1}^{n} a_{kj}x_i$ have a significant fundamental at the particular period and phase.

The example of the previous section falls into this class. Indeed let us define for each oscillator a variable

$$y_i = \dot{x}_i \tag{7.6.4}$$

and then write Eqs. (7.3.1), (7.5.6), and (7.5.7) together as

$$\dot{y}_i = \varepsilon f_i(x_i, y_i) - \omega^2(1 - r)x_i - r\omega^2 z_i \tag{7.6.5}$$

$$z_i = \sum_{j=1}^{n} x_j = s \tag{7.6.6}$$

It can be easily seen that the solution corresponding to ω_1 is a first-order synchronization and the solution corresponding to ω_2 a second-order synchronization.

Figure 7.6.1 illustrates an arrangement corresponding to a second-order synchronization.

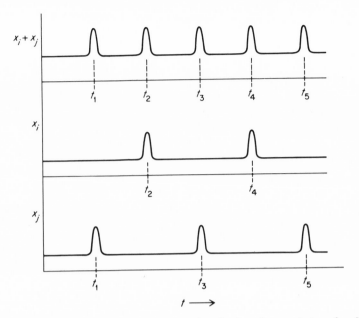

FIG. 7.6.1.   Illustration of second-order synchronization of a population of oscillators: x_i and x_j are the amplitudes of two units belonging to the two groups oscillating in phase opposition.

We consider next the question of stability of the various states of synchronization.

A perturbation of Eqs. (7.6.1)–(7.6.3) leads to the following expressions, if x_k is replaced by $x_k + \xi_k$ and y_k by $y_k + \eta_k$:

$$dx_k/dt + d\xi_k/dt = f_k(x_k + \xi_k , y_k + \eta_k , z_k + \zeta_k) \qquad (7.6.7)$$

$$dy_k/dt + d\eta_k/dt = g_k(x_k + \xi_k , y_k + \eta_k , z_k + \zeta_k) \qquad (7.6.8)$$

$$z_k + \zeta_k = \mathscr{F}\left(\sum_{j=1}^{n} a_{kj}(x_j + \xi_j)\right) \qquad (7.6.9)$$

The first two can be simplified by a Taylor expansion into

$$\frac{d\xi_k}{dt} = \frac{\partial f_k}{\partial x_k}\,\xi_k + \frac{\partial f_k}{\partial y_k}\,\eta_k + \frac{\partial f_k}{\partial z_k}\,\zeta_k \qquad (7.6.10)$$

$$\frac{d\eta_k}{dt} = \frac{\partial g_k}{\partial x_k}\,\xi_k + \frac{\partial g_k}{\partial y_k}\,\eta_k + \frac{\partial g_k}{\partial z_k}\,\zeta_k \qquad (7.6.11)$$

If $\mathscr{F}$ is a scalar operator and furthermore continuous and differentiable, then the Eq. (7.6.9) can also be simplified into

$$\zeta_k = F \cdot \sum_{j=1}^{n} a_{kj} \xi_j \tag{7.6.12}$$

where F is the derivative of $\mathscr{F}$ with respect to its argument.

All the partial derivatives are computed along a solution. Thus the question of stability is reduced to the study of the system of the linear, time-varying equations (7.6.10)–(7.6.12).

At this point it is worth noticing that the system of Eqs. (7.6.1)–(7.6.3) can be easily modified to describe oscillations of a continuum. Indeed they can be rewritten as

$$\partial x(\mathbf{p}, t)/\partial t = f(\mathbf{p}, x, y, z) \tag{7.6.13}$$

$$\partial y(\mathbf{p}, t)/\partial t = g(\mathbf{p}, x, y, z) \tag{7.6.14}$$

$$z(\mathbf{p}) = \mathscr{F}\left[\int\int_R A(\mathbf{p}, \mathbf{q}) x(\mathbf{q}, t)\, d\mathbf{q}\right] \tag{7.6.15}$$

where $\mathbf{p}$ is a space coordinate and R the region of interaction. For $\mathbf{p} = $ const, Eqs. (7.6.13) and (7.6.14) describe a single oscillator.

In this case higher-order synchronization corresponds to stationary waves in the continuum R.

We will show examples of both the discrete and continuous case in the next chapter in terms of specific biochemical systems.

7.7 Concluding Remarks

The previous analysis illustrates many features peculiar to populations of interacting oscillators:

(i) They may have more than one stable state of synchronization, each one with its own frequency of oscillations. Thus after a disturbance the system may return to a different limit cycle than the one it was on before.

(ii) The possibility of multifrequency oscillations exists (macroscopically observed usually as almost periodic). If the coupling is weak, one expects that the states of stable synchronization may not be reachable from arbitrary initial conditions or after a disturbance has moved the system away from a limit cycle.

(iii) The macroscopic behavior of such systems depends on the average value of its parameters rather than their values in individual units. Thus they are usually quite insensitive to small variations of the latter. However, the opposite tends to be true for the variations of the average values. Since this is a point often disputed in the literature we will illustrate it by a numerical example:

Equation (7.5.17) gives the frequency of oscillations of a population of identical oscillators:

$$\omega_1 = \omega[1 + r(n - 1)]^{1/2}$$

For a given r one can calculate the ratio ω_1/ω for various values of n and then compare the respective changes in values. This is done in Table 7.7.1, together with the study of the effects of changes in r for a given n.

TABLE 7.7.1

			Change in:	
r	n	ω_1/ω	parameter	ω_1/ω
0.01	5	1.02		
0.01	7	1.03	40%	~1%
−0.18	5	0.53		
−0.18	6	0.316	20%	~40%
−0.18	7	No oscillations (negative radical)	40%	∞
−0.010	11	0.945		
−0.020	11	0.895	100%	~5%
−0.10	10	0.316		
−0.12	10	No oscillations (negative radical)	20%	∞

Depending on the value of r, the system may be quite sensitive in changes of n and vice versa.

(iv) The frequency of oscillations may depend significantly on the coupling strength, and therefore the frequency of synchronization in a population may be quite different than the individual frequencies of the oscillators.

The biological significance of these and other features will be discussed in the next chapter.

7.8 Bibliographical Notes

The concept of structural stability was investigated by the Russian mathematicians in the early 1930s [And-I, Bog-I]. Closely related to it is the notion of bifurcation, of the qualitative change in the behavior of a system when one of its parameters passes through a critical value.

The asymptotic techniques are also due to Russian mathematicians, and the notes on Section 1.5 are pertinent here too.

Technical applications of systems consisting of a large number of coupled oscillators have been scant. The best known relates to the problem of synchronization in a communications network. This has been studied by Pierce, Sandberg, and others [Pie-1, San-1, San-2]. However, the mathematical formulation they use reduces the problem to one of finding the equilibria of a high-order system rather than the periodic solutions. This is achieved by using the frequencies as state variables. (Each station measures frequency differences.) Such an approach is difficult to justify for the case of biological systems.

Kemer and later Goodwin studied populations of oscillators as conservative systems which could be directly integrated [Goo-A]. Winfree studied the case of weakly coupled oscillators where the limit cycles of the individual units in the presence of interaction are close to the ones in the absence of interactions [Win-0]. Walker has studied interacting oscillators through Liapunov's method and computer simulation. The basic simplification in his study was the assumption that only one essential nonlinearity was present [Wal-1]. For this case however the describing function (Section 1.6) or Popov's theorem are more helpful [Aiz-I].

The material of Sections 5 and 6 has appeared in a preliminary form in a series of papers by Pavlidis [Pav-8, Pav-11, Pav-12].

Some efforts on rigorous solutions can be found in the literature [Agg-1, Agg-2, Jen-1, Mos-1]. The problem has also been studied in the case of interacting models of neural oscillators [Dun-3, Dun-4]. It probably typifies the class of problems mentioned by Fomin [Fom-1], where the presently available mathematical tools are inadequate for biological problems.

CHAPTER 8

Biological Phenomena Attributable to Populations of Oscillators

8.1 Introduction

We have seen in the previous chapter the salient features of systems of coupled nonlinear oscillators. Probably the most important is the multiplicity of stable solutions which predict that after a, possibly minor, disturbance one can observe a drastic change in the macroscopic dynamical behavior of the system (e.g., doubling of the frequency of oscillations).

From a biological viewpoint one should expect that any rhythm regulator at the cellular level should consist of a group of coupled oscillators.* This would give a more reliable system because of redundancy. In this way the organism is guarded not only against "loosing its clock" but also against the effects of random parameter variations. Since the behavior of the system depends primarily on the average values of parameters among various units, it tends to be rather stable. Even if the value in a single unit changed drastically, the value of the average will be affected very little.

A number of experimental results exist which would be difficult to explain without assuming some kind of a population of oscillators. Alternative explanations, if at all possible, require rather complex models of a single unit. In this respect the law of parsimony works in favor of the system of many simple units.

In a limiting case, if the number of units is very large, such a system can behave as a continuum of oscillators and it can be described by a

---

* By this we mean units of similar function existing in many "copies" [Har-A] rather than of different function [Pit-1, Pit-2, Pit-3].

single partial differential equation rather than a system of ordinary ones. This offers certain advantages for its simplified mathematical analysis. Section 8.4 deals with an example of this approach applied to the study of patterns in cultures of fungi.

8.2 Frequency Doubling in Circadian Rhythms

Investigators of locomotor rhythms have often observed "peculiar" response in free-running animals. In the case of a system controlled

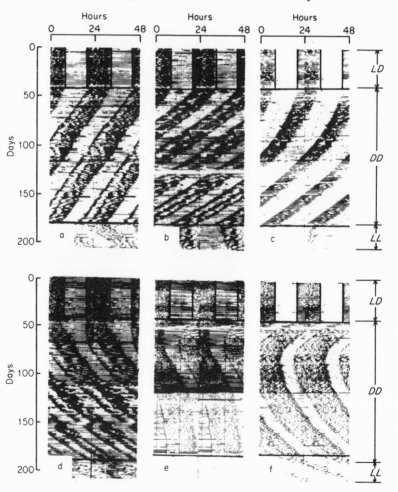

FIG. 8.2.1. The circadian rhythm of locomotor activity in 6 deermice (Peromyscus bardii), A–F [Pit-9].

by a single oscillator one would expect its period to remain constant or vary monotonically with time (as a result of parameter variation). However, what one observes is often quite different from that simple picture. Figures 8.2.1 and 8.2.2 show a few examples of "peculiar"

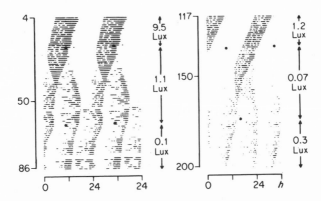

FIG. 8.2.2.   Illustration of frequency doubling (rhythm splitting) in the locomotor activity of a tree shrew (Tupaia) [Hof-7, Hof-10].

behavior [Pit-9, Hof-7]. We should emphasize that one can reproduce much of such behavior with oscillators with one degree of freedom and the simultaneous change of one or more parameters by rather elaborate time patterns. This approach however begs the question since one would like to know what causes the particular time patterns.

A simple model of some of these phenomena can be provided by the system of Section 7.6. The doubling of frequency shown in Fig. 8.2.2 can be attributed to a switch from a first-order to a second-order synchronization which in turn was triggered by the earlier change in light intensity. Indeed consider the limit cycle I shown in Fig. 8.2.3. The arc AB represents the distribution of states of nonidentical oscillators under first-order synchronization for light intensity L_1. For light intensity L_2 the limit cycle will be different, as, for example, shown by II. During the transition from I to II different units will follow different paths (broken lines) and a loss of synchronization will result. If they are weakly coupled (under L_2), then they may not be able to reach a first-order synchronization but only a second order (Regions CD and EF).

However, this is not the only possible explanation of the phenomenon. Indeed consider a system consisting of two oscillators, A and B. A drives B while B has no effect on A. The frequency of A depends on light intensity while that of B is independent of the level of illumination. Figure 8.2.4 shows a hypothetical law of change of ω_A versus light

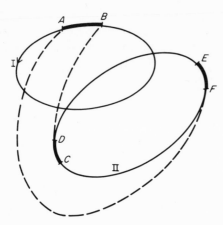

FIG. 8.2.3.   Loss of synchrony in a population of oscillators due to a transition from limit cycle I to limit cycle II.

intensity L. When ω_A and ω_B are close, then one expects A to entrain B so that the observed frequency $\omega_B' = \omega_A$. However, when ω_A becomes considerably lower than ω_B entrainment is not possible and instead superharmonic entrainment may take place (see Chapter 4) where B is entrained to twice the frequency of A, $\omega_B' = 2\omega_A$. If the overt behavior represents the frequency of B a doubling of the frequency will be observed when L crosses the value L^*.

Note that according to either model the new frequency is not exactly twice the old one when L changes because of the simultaneous direct effect of L on the frequency of oscillations. This is certainly compatible

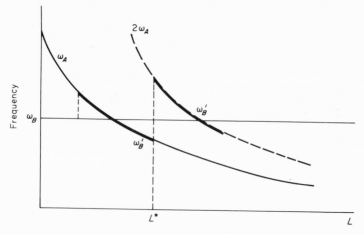

FIG. 8.2.4.   The dependence of the frequency ω_A of a driving oscillator on the light intensity L causes the entrained frequency of a driven oscillator ω_B' to follow the variation along the heavy lines. L^* is the intensity causing a frequency doubling.

with the data of Fig. 8.2.2. Also neither explanation makes any assumptions about details of the structure of the oscillators.

It is worthwhile to follow this discussion one step further and ask what other properties of the system behavior are predicted by either model. The following is a list of such phenomena.

(1) The change in frequency should present a hysteresis effect in terms of light intensity. In the first model this is expected because the region of attraction of the second-order synchronization is in general smaller than that of the first. Indeed the change from one state of synchronization to another is caused by the temporary "dispersal" of the various units. Thus if they are already in two groups it is easier to keep them that way then to go from one into two. A similar argument holds for the second model because superharmonic entrainment is less stable than harmonic entrainment. Thus, if going from intensity L_1 to L_2 $(L_1 < L_2)$ causes a doubling of the frequency, going from L_2 to L_1 will not necessarily cause a halving. Rather it may be necessary to go to L_3 $(L_3 < L_1)$ to achieve the lower frequency. If one recalls that the stability properties of second-order synchronization reflect those of subharmonic entrainment, then he can see that the two mechanisms suggested are not very different in this respect.

(2) In the first model the disturbance of a synchronous state is essential for producing the frequency doubling. Thus, if the change in light intensity is gradual (for example, over a day or two) rather than sudden, no phase dispersal of units will occur and thus the phenomenon will not be observed. Note that no matter how weak is the coupling a stable first-order synchronization is always possible, although with small region of attraction. On the other hand, in the second model the increase in frequency must eventually occur regardless of the way the light intensity is changed. The only difference would possibly be in the value at which the change occurs.

(3) In the first model one should be able to observe cases of third- or higher-order synchronization, at least temporarily. This would not occur in the second model unless the light intensity was changed sufficiently to cause a synchronization to the third (or higher) harmonic.

(4) From Fig. 8.2.4 it is obvious that the frequency doubling should be caused by a change of light intensity in the direction which causes a decrease in frequency. If one had assumed that ω_A was fixed and ω_B was a function of light intensity, he would have reached the opposite conclusion. However, in this case the observed frequency would be independent of light intensity except for discrete jumps (from ω_A to $2\omega_A$). This contradicts the observations discussed in Chapter 5 and therefore

we have to associate with the second model the prediction based on Fig. 8.2.4. The mechanism suggested by the first model allows no particular predictions about the correlation between the direction of change of light intensity and the occurrence of the splitting.

We may now turn our attention to the experimental observations and compare them with these predictions: The first investigator to observe this phenomenon was Pittendrigh [Pit-3, Pit-9] in hamsters (*Mescocricetus auratus*), and then Roberts [Rob-1] in cockroaches (*Leucophaea maderae*) and Swade [Swa-1, Swa-4] in the deermouse (*Peromyscus maniculatus*). However its first systematic study was made by Hoffman [Hof-7, Hof-10], who used the tree shrew (*Tupaia belangeri*). There he observed that the frequency doubling was caused by a decrease in light intensity and he also observed significant hysteresis as predicted by (1) above. Although Tupaia is a diurnal animal, the frequency of its locomotor rhythm is a decreasing function of light intensity and this does not contradict the second model on the basis of prediction (4). Since neither Hoffman nor anyone else has made experiments on the basis of gradual changes in light intensity it is not possible to test prediction (2). However in a few experiments more than two peaks of activity were observed during 24 hours. Usually a third peak appeared and then merged. In view of prediction (3) this seems to be evidence in favor of the first model.

In the earlier experiments the doubling occurred in transferring nocturnal animals in constant light [Pit-9, Rob-1] or increasing the minimum of intensity in a fluctuating light cycle [Swa-1, Swa-4]. In all cases light also caused a decrease in frequency, and therefore prediction (4) is not disproved.

The mechanisms described here may also be used to explain the two-peak patterns of activity in birds observed by Aschoff [Asc-5]. Alternative models for explaining such patterns do not suggest why the peaks are about 12 hours apart [Sel-5, Wev-2]. Frequency doubling under various conditions has also been reported by Kramer [Kra-1].

Before concluding this discussion we should mention that the usual term for this phenomenon in the literature is *rhythm splitting*. However this term has been used for other phenomena and, in particular, for the loss of synchrony between two rhythms involving different activities in the same organism (e.g., locomotion and temperature changes) [Asc-7, Asc-10]. Furthermore the salient feature of the 180° phase difference between the two peaks is not indicated by this term. Although the change in frequency is rarely exactly doubling (because of the simultaneous direct effect of light on frequency) we feel that the term *frequency doubling* is more appropriate.

8.3   A System of Coupled Biochemical Oscillators

The discussion of the previous section was quite abstract and one can question the existence of systems with the assumed dynamical properties in living organisms. This is in particular true about the population of coupled oscillators with more than one synchronous state. We will present here a specific model which can be described in terms of chemical kinetics and, in particular, the biochemical reactions discussed in Section 3.6. We assume that we have many such units in a given environment (e.g., one per cell). We further assume that the concentration of G at time t is common for all the units (e.g., G is uniformly distributed in the interstitial fluid) and that it is affected by the total concentration of X at some earlier time $t - \tau$. (For example, the products of the reactions in each unit are returned outside the cell. They are mixed there and their total concentration reacts with G. The proportionality to X is a simplifying assumption.) Before we write the equations of the population of oscillators, we proceed to introduce a set of normalized variables in the one-unit model [Hig-2, Pav-9].

Let us define

$$d' = x/A_1, \qquad y' = Y/C, \qquad t' = tB_1/C, \qquad z = A_1/C, \qquad d = D/B_1$$

$$a = A/A_1C(=k_4k_5/k_6k_7), \qquad b = B_2/B_1$$

Then Eqs. (3.6.4)–(3.6.6) are simplified into

$$dx'/dt' = z(d - v') \tag{8.3.1}$$

$$dy'/dt' = v' - by'/(1 + y') \tag{8.3.2}$$

$$v' = \frac{x'y'}{[y'(1 + x') + a]} \tag{8.3.3}$$

Using these equations the model of the interacting units can be described by the following system [Pav-11]:

$$\frac{dx_k}{dt} = \xi \left(d_0 + p' \sum_{i=1}^{n} x_i(t - \tau) - v_k \right) \tag{8.3.4}$$

$$\frac{dy_k}{dt} = v_k - \frac{by_k}{(1 + y_k)} \tag{8.3.5}$$

$$v_k = \frac{x_k y_k}{[y_k(1 + x_k) + a]} \tag{8.3.6}$$

where p' is a coupling coefficient.

The above description assumes identical units (see Section 7.5). In the case of first-order synchronization, Eqs. (8.3.5) and (8.3.6) reduce to Eqs. (8.3.2) and (8.3.3) while Eq. (8.3.4) becomes

$$dx/dt = \xi[d_0 + px(t - \tau) - v] \qquad (8.3.7)$$

where $p = np'$. The study of this equation is not easy because of the delay τ. Assuming $\tau = 0$ it becomes

$$dx/dt = \xi(d_0 + px - v) \qquad (8.3.8)$$

It is easily found that

$$\frac{dx}{dt} = 0 \quad \text{for} \quad y = \frac{-a(d_0 + px)}{px^2 + x(p + t - 1) + d_0} \qquad (8.3.9)$$

$$\frac{dy}{dt} = 0 \quad \text{for} \quad x = \frac{b(y + a)}{1 + y(1 - b)} \qquad (8.3.10)$$

Figures 8.3.1 and 8.3.2 show the phase plane portrait of the system for $p < 0$ and $p > 0$.

Because of the physical meaning of x and y, only the first quadrant is considered. For negative p it is easily seen that an intersection of the two curves for $\dot{x} = 0$ and $\dot{y} = 0$ will occur only if

$$p > -d_0/ab \qquad (8.3.11)$$

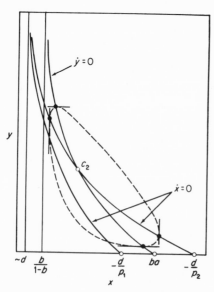

FIG. 8.3.1. Phase plane portrait of first-order synchronization for $p < 0$ [Pav-11].

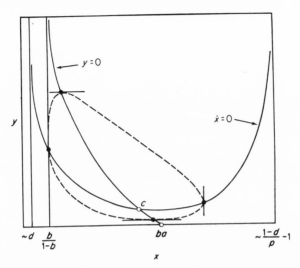

FIG. 8.3.2.   Phase plane portrait of first-order synchronization for $p > 0$ [Pav-11].

A study of the phase plane portrait through the method of isoclines indicates that for positive p it is necessary that the abscissa of the asymptote must be substantially greater than ab. Thus a second constraint on p is derived as

$$p \ll (1 - d_0)/ab \qquad (8.3.12)$$

Equations (8.3.11) and (8.3.12) give the limits for the coupling coefficient p (or p' for a given n). If the first condition is violated, then the system reaches a state of equilibrium with $y = 0$ and x at some value less than ab. The physical interpretation of this situation is that when the "wastes" of the cells (the term $p'x_i$) interfere substantially with their "food supply" (d_0) stagnation occurs. If Eq. (8.3.12) is violated, then the system becomes unstable. In this case, the "wastes" contribute substantially to the "food supply" and a "population explosion" occurs.

The addition of a nonzero delay in Eq. (8.3.8) is expected to stabilize the situation when the feedback is positive ($p > 0$) and to contribute to instability or oscillations if the feedback is negative ($p < 0$). Thus, in the presence of delay one may expect stable oscillations for values of p outside the limits imposed by Eqs. (8.3.11) and (8.3.12).

Since a further analysis of the above system is not possible because of its highly nonlinear character, computer simulation was used. The system of Eqs. (8.3.4)–(8.3.6) was simulated through a FORTRAN program on a computer using the following values for its coefficients: $a = 30$, b was varied between 0.05 and 0.30, $d_0 = 0.03$, $z = 0.167$, p

was varied between -0.005 and 0.02, n was varied between 3 and 15, and τ was varied between 0 and 1500. Also y was required to be at least equal to 0.001. This was the same choice of values as for the single-unit system described originally by Higgins [Hig-2] and used later for the simulation of circadian rhythms [Pav-9]. The period of a single unit for $b = 0.1$ and $p' = 0$ is $T_0 = 1210$. If one wants to think strictly in terms of circadian rhythms, he may use the correspondence of 1.2 min for each unit of time of the model. This gives $T_0 = 24.2$ hours.

The simulation produced cases of both first-order (FOS) and higher-order synchronization (HOS). Figure 8.3.3 shows an example of second-order synchronization. In general if the coupling was strong enough FOS would be achieved regardless of initial conditions. Otherwise (for weak coupling) the latter would determine whether the system achieved FOS, HOS, or failed to synchronize at all.

Figures 8.3.4 and 8.3.5 summarize the results of the simulation. The following are the main conclusions:

A. For weak coupling (low value of p) the period T is an increasing function of b. The rate of increase becomes less for stronger coupling and eventually the relation is reversed. First-order synchrony is observed in all these cases. However, when b becomes large enough then higher-order synchrony is observed while at some intermediate values the various units may fail to synchronize.

B. For a given b the period is an increasing function of the coupling

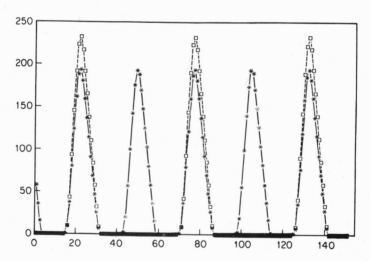

FIG. 8.3.3.   Second-order synchronization observed in computer simulation. The broken line is $y_1(t)$ and the full line is the sum of the y_k's (under a different scale) [Pav-11].

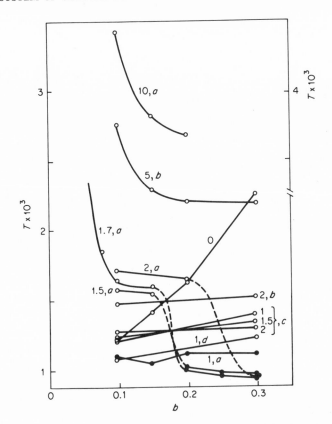

F<small>IG.</small> 8.3.4.   Plot of the period versus b. Each curve is marked by the value of p times 10^2 and a letter denoting the delay: $a = 500$, $b = 250$, $c = 100$, $d = 0$. The curve $10/a$ is according to the scale to the right. Simple circles denote FOS; full circles HOS or asynchrony [Pav-11].

strength and the number of interacting units and first-order synchrony is always observed for high values of p. For lower values of p higher-order synchrony becomes possible and for very weak coupling the various units behave independently.

C. The period is an increasing function of the delay time τ and the value of the delay mitigates the occurrence of the phenomena described in A and B.

D. With one or two exceptions the only high-order synchronizations achieved were of second order only where the two groups of oscillators have a phase difference equal to 180° (half a period). In one case with a very long transient a single unit wandered for a while before "catching on" to one of the two groups already formed.

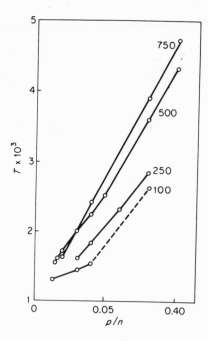

FIG. 8.3.5.   Plot of the period T versus p/n for various delays [Pav-11].

These results simulate the splitting of circadian rhythms as described in the previous section, at least in general form. If we assume, as in the single-unit case (Section 3.6), that b is an increasing function of light intensity, then the frequency doubling occurs for a change in light intensity, which, in the case of strongly coupled units, also causes a decrease in the period or an increase in the frequency. This is in contrast to the results showing that the "doubling" is caused by a change in the direction of decreasing frequency. One might conclude that the units of the circadian clock are weakly coupled but this is not necessarily so. Modifications of the model can allow for agreement between simulation and experimental results even for strongly coupled units.

8.4   Spatial Organization of Populations of Oscillators and an Interpretation of the Patterns of Zonation of Fungi Cultures

The main conclusion of the previous section is that a rather simple (conceptually) system of interacting biochemical oscillators can show the feature of multiple states of synchronization. We could continue discussing various phenomena in terms of such a "realistic" model, but there are at least two reasons against doing this.

(a) We would be dealing with an "overspecified" system, and it would not be easy to distinguish between properties inherent to a class of models and those peculiar to a particular member of the class. (This is the case for the results discussed in the last paragraph of the previous section.)

(b) The mathematical analysis of systems of equations of chemical kinetics is often impossible and one has to use computer simulation which requires additional specification of the model.

Using abstract models avoids overspecification (this was done in Section 8.2). If it is necessary to use a specific mathematical system, then we will decide in favor of simplicity. This will make mathematical analysis possible and it would be less likely to impose model-peculiar features.

Along these lines we introduce the following model for a system of interacting dynamical units: We assume that they are numerous enough to justify replacing a system of ordinary differential equations by a single partial differential equation and that a linearization of the system is also justified. Let $x(\mathbf{p}, t)$ denote the output of the system at a point $\mathbf{p}$ at time t, $\mathbf{p}$ is a vector of space coordinates. Then we consider a system described by an equation which is a special case of that described by Eqs. (7.6.13)–(7.6.15):

$$\frac{\partial^2 x(\mathbf{p}, t)}{\partial t^2} + \alpha\,\frac{\partial x(\mathbf{p}, t)}{\partial t} + \omega_0^2 \int_R A(\mathbf{p}, \mathbf{q})\, x(\mathbf{q}, t)\, dv = 0 \qquad (8.4.1)$$

where $A(\mathbf{p}, \mathbf{q})$ denotes the effect of the oscillation at the point $\mathbf{q}$ to that at the point $\mathbf{p}$ and α is a damping coefficient. The integral is over the volume where the reactions take place. This can be further simplified by expressing

$$x(\mathbf{p}, t) = P(\mathbf{p})T(t) \qquad (8.4.2)$$

Substituting this into Eq. (8.4.1) yields

$$\left(\frac{d^2 T}{dt^2} + \alpha\,\frac{dT}{dt}\right) P(\mathbf{p}) + T(t)\, \omega_0^2 \int_R A(\mathbf{p}, \mathbf{q})\, P(\mathbf{q})\, dv = 0 \qquad (8.4.3)$$

or

$$d^2 T/dt^2 + \alpha\, dT/dt + \lambda \omega_0^2 T = 0 \qquad (8.4.4)$$

and

$$\int_R A(\mathbf{p}, \mathbf{q})\, P(\mathbf{q})\, dv = \lambda P(\mathbf{p}) \qquad (8.4.5)$$

It is a well-known theorem of the theory of partial differential equations that the general solution of Eq. (8.4.1) can be expressed by an infinite weighted sum of special solutions of the form (8.4.2) [Chu-I].

For a certain range of the values of λ the solution of Eq. (8.4.4) will be periodic and its frequency will depend explicitly on λ. In turn, λ and $P(\mathbf{p})$ are determined by the coupling factor $A(\mathbf{p}, \mathbf{q})$. They are the eigenvalues and eigenfunctions of the integral operator

$$\int_R A(\mathbf{p}, \mathbf{q}) \cdot dv \tag{8.4.6}$$

It is obvious that in general different eigenvalues will correspond to different eigenfunctions, and thus a sum of terms like the one in Eq. (8.4.2) will not always represent a monofrequency oscillation. We will describe next certain cases where this is possible.

Let $A(\mathbf{p}, \mathbf{q})$ depend only on the norm of the difference $\mathbf{p} - \mathbf{q}$ and let R be a region with $\mathbf{p}$ as a center of symmetry (it could be the whole space). This is a reasonable assumption and it simply means that the effect of one oscillator on another depends only on their distance. Then Eq. (8.4.5) can be written as

$$\int_{R(\mathbf{p})} A(\mathbf{p} - \mathbf{q}) P(\mathbf{q}) \, dv = \lambda P(\mathbf{p}) \tag{8.4.7}$$

Let $\mathbf{y} = \mathbf{p} - \mathbf{q}$. This is a shift of coordinates and the new volume differential du will be unchanged except for the sign; i.e., $du = -dv$. Also the region of integration will not depend explicitly on $\mathbf{p}$ because of the center-symmetry assumption. Then Eq. (8.4.7) becomes

$$-\int_{R'} A(\mathbf{y}) P(\mathbf{p} - \mathbf{y}) \, du = \lambda P(\mathbf{p}) \tag{8.4.8}$$

Obviously if $P(\mathbf{p} - \mathbf{y}) = P(\mathbf{p})P(-\mathbf{y})$ this equation will be satisfied with

$$\lambda = -\int_{R'} A(\mathbf{y}) P(-\mathbf{y}) \, du \tag{8.4.9}$$

It is also well known that the only functions with that property are exponentials; i.e., for some constant K and constant vector $\mathbf{c}$,

$$P(\mathbf{p}) = K \, e^{\langle \mathbf{c}, \mathbf{p} \rangle} \tag{8.4.10}$$

where the exponent denotes the scalar product of the vectors $\mathbf{c}$ and $\mathbf{p}$. If $\mathbf{c}$ is imaginary, say $i\omega$, then $P(\mathbf{p})$ can be written as

$$P(\mathbf{p}) = K[\cos(\langle \omega, \mathbf{p} \rangle) + i \sin(\langle \omega, \mathbf{p} \rangle)] \tag{8.4.11}$$

It can be shown easily that $K \cos(\langle \omega, \mathbf{p} \rangle)$ and $K \sin(\langle \omega, \mathbf{p} \rangle)$ are also eigenfunctions.*

Note that the form of the last two expressions is independent of the exact form of interaction as long as each point is affected by its neighbors in a way depending only on their mutual distance (this implies also the assumption about the center symmetry of R). On the other hand, the eigenvalues λ depend on the exact form of the interaction as shown by Eq. (8.4.9). Because of Eq. (8.4.4) the same will be true for the frequency of the oscillations in the time domain. The following examples illustrate various special cases:

EXAMPLE 8.4.1. If the spatial organization of the oscillators is one dimensional, e.g., along an array, then Eqs. (8.4.7) and (8.4.9)–(8.4.11) become

$$\int_{p-L}^{p+L} A(p - q)\, P(q)\, dq = \lambda\, P(p) \tag{8.4.7'}$$

$$\lambda = \int_{-L}^{L} A(y)\, e^{-cy}\, dy \tag{8.4.9'}$$

$$P(p) = K\, e^{cp} \tag{8.4.10'}$$

$$P(p) = K'\, \cos(\omega p) \tag{8.4.11'}$$

EXAMPLE 8.4.2. If the oscillators lie all on a plane (or a surface topologically equivalent) and we use polar coordinates, Eq. (8.4.11) becomes

$$P(r, \phi) = K'\, \cos(\omega_1 r + \omega_2 \phi + \beta) \tag{8.4.11''}$$

For $\beta = 0$, $\omega_2 = 0$ the maxima of $P(r, \phi)$ form concentric circles around the origin. Otherwise their locations satisfy the equation

$$\omega_1 r + \omega_2 \phi + \beta = 2k\pi \tag{8.4.12}$$

---

* Indeed, using a trigonometric formula, we have

$$\int_{R'} A(\mathbf{y}) \cos(\langle \omega, \mathbf{p} - \mathbf{y} \rangle)\, du = \cos(\langle \omega, \mathbf{p} \rangle) \int_{R'} A(\mathbf{y}) \cos(\langle \omega, \mathbf{y} \rangle)\, du$$

$$+ \sin(\langle \omega, \mathbf{p} \rangle) \int_{R'} A(\mathbf{y}) \sin(\langle \omega, \mathbf{y} \rangle)\, du$$

Because the kernel $A(\mathbf{y})$ depends only on the norm of its argument and because of the symmetry of the region of integration, the last integral is zero. A similar calculation can be made for $\sin(\langle \omega, p \rangle)$.

The above expression represents a family of Archimedean spirals, each one with a path equal to $-2\pi\omega_2/\omega_1$ while the distance between adjacent pairs of spirals (for various values of k) is $2\pi/\omega_1$. It is obvious that, if $\omega_2 = -1$, then only a single spiral of maxima will be observed while, if $\omega_2 = -1/m$ (m an integer), m spirals of maxima will occur.

EXAMPLE 8.4.3. In order to estimate the eigenvalues we consider a special case of the previous example; namely, we assume that the interaction is governed by

$$A(r, \phi, \rho, \theta) = \begin{cases} 1/\rho & \text{if } |r - \rho| < \varepsilon, \text{ and } |\phi - \theta| < \delta \\ 0 & \text{otherwise} \end{cases} \tag{8.4.13}$$

Then Eq. (8.4.7) becomes

$$\int_{r+\varepsilon}^{r-\varepsilon} \int_{\phi+\delta}^{\phi+\delta} P(\rho, \theta)\, d\rho\, d\theta = \lambda\, P(r, \phi) \tag{8.4.14}$$

Note that, since $dv = \rho\, d\rho\, d\theta$, the $1/\rho$ of Eq. (8.4.13) is cancelled out. The effect of that choice is to give the same amount of interaction among adjacent units, regardless of distance from the origin. Indeed the area of the sector where $A \neq 0$ is equal to $4\rho\varepsilon\delta$, and if we had left A constant we would have a system where the farther a unit is from the origin the more it is affected by its neighbors.

Although Eqs. (8.4.13) and (8.4.14) do not describe exactly symmetrical interactions, one can easily verify that the eigenfunction $P(r, \varphi)$ is of the same form as (8.4.11″) and (8.4.12″). Equation (8.4.9) is now

$$\lambda = \int_{-\varepsilon}^{\varepsilon} \int_{-\delta}^{\delta} P(r + r_1, \varphi + \varphi_1)\, dr_1\, d\varphi_1 \tag{8.4.15}$$

For $P(r, \varphi)$ of the form given by Eq. (8.4.11″) this yields

$$\lambda = \frac{4 \sin(\omega_1 \varepsilon) \sin(\omega_2 \delta)}{\omega_1 \omega_2} \tag{8.4.16}$$

If ε and δ are sufficiently small, then the above expression is simplified to

$$\lambda \simeq 4\varepsilon\delta \tag{8.4.17}$$

i.e., for all the eigenfunctions the eigenvalues are approximately equal to the area of interaction and the time domain frequency for all of them will be

$$\omega_t \simeq 2\omega_0(\varepsilon\delta)^{1/2} \tag{8.4.18}$$

The last two examples point out to an explanation of patterns observed in fungi cultures [Bour-1, Win-4, Win-6] (see also Section 2.7).

It has been reported that concentric rings are observed at 60% of the cases while the remaining show Archimedean spirals. Double spirals are rare. In terms of the present model this would mean that the prevalent values of ω_2 are either 0 (for concentratic circles) or -1 (for single spirals), while in-between values (for multiple spirals) are rare. In all cases the frequency in the time domain is independent of the pattern, which is in agreement with Eq. (8.4.18). The important remaining question is what factor determines the mode of the solution of Eq. (8.4.1). Mathematically this is determined by the initial and boundary conditions. If the growth is in an infinite medium, then one must evaluate the Fourier transform of the initial distribution [Chu-I]. Then the solution will be the integral of this expression times $T(t)$ with respect to the parameters ω_1 and ω_2. Since the exact shape of the initial distribution is not generally known, such a calculation is not possible. A qualitative observation is that, if the initial distribution is symmetrical

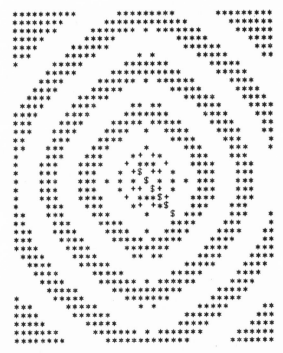

FIG. 8.4.1. Concentrating circular patterns obtained in computer simulation of Eq. (8.4.1) with interaction law given by Eq. (8.4.19). A *, +, or $ denotes a point where x exceeds a given threshold. The bounds of the printout are exactly those of the integration domain.

around the origin, then the problem is one dimensional and the only fluctuations can occur as a function of the distance from the origin. This will give rise to circular patterns. If the initial distribution is antisymmetrical, then both variables will appear in the Fourier transform and spiral patterns are expected.

A computer simulation (through a FORTRAN program) of Eq. (8.4.1) with $\alpha = 0$ and

$$A(\mathbf{p}, \mathbf{q}) = \frac{1}{|p_1 - q_1| + |p_2 - q_2|} \qquad (8.4.19)$$

gave a circular pattern when the initial distribution was equal to 1 at a single point (Fig. 8.4.1), interfering circular patterns when it was equal to 1 at two distant points (Fig. 8.4.2), and spirals when it was equal to −1 and 1, respectively, at two adjacent groups of points (Fig. 8.4.3).

We should also emphasize that the occurrence of the zonation patterns does not require that $T(t)$ be periodic functions in the time domain. Other forms of equations besides (8.4.1) can lead to similar conclusions

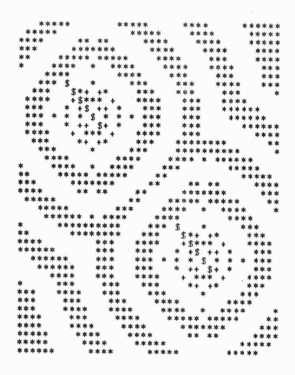

FIG. 8.4.2. Merging of circular patterns for two starting points; otherwise same as in Fig. (8.4.1).

FIG. 8.4.3. Spiral pattern obtained by simulation similar to Fig. 8.4.1 but with different initial conditions.

as long as their space component $P(\mathbf{p})$ satisfies an integral equation of the form given by Eq. (8.4.5) with a kernel which has periodic eigenfunctions. This is a difference with the model of the phenomenon described by Winfree [Win-4, Win-6], where the oscillations in the time domain are essential. His model also predicts the topological form of the patterns (closed curves or spirals) but not their exact shape (circles or Archimedean spirals).

The results are also related to the predicted oscillations in space on the basis of thermodynamic and other theoretical considerations [Lav-1, Lef-2, Oth-1] and those observed experimentally [Bus-1, Zai-1].

8.5 The Relation between Frequency and Tissue Size

Equation (7.5.17) shows that under certain conditions the observed frequency of oscillations depends on the number n of interacting units. It was derived under the assumption that all units interact with each other. If they do so in an inhibitory way ($r < 0$), then ω is a decreasing function of n while the opposite is true if they interact in excitory way ($r > 0$). If $r = 1$, then $\omega_1 = \omega_0\sqrt{n}$. This expression is similar to Eq. (8.4.18), which can be written as $\omega_t = \omega_0(4\delta\varepsilon)^{1/2}$. The quantity under the radical is the area of interaction, and for the discrete case it corresponds exactly to the number of interacting units.

A physical system where there is a dependence between frequency and size has been described by Jacklet [Jac-3]. The preparation consisted of parts of the retina of the sea slug *Aplysia californica*. The isolated whole eye exhibits periodic bursts of neuronal activity. The frequency of bursts has a circadian rhythm ($\tau \cong 28$ hours) with maxima up to 200 per half hour and minima close to zero (see Section 2.6 for similar neuronal rhythms). If part of the retina is removed surgically, then a decrease in the period of oscillations τ is observed. The decrease is rather slow till 80 % of the retina is removed (it drops from 28 to 25 hours) but it becomes very rapid afterwards, dropping to less than 3 hours.

The period T_1 equals $2\pi/\omega_1$ and it can be made an increasing function of n if ω_1 is a decreasing function of that variable; i.e., if the units interact in an inhibitory way ($r < 0$), then Eq. (7.5.17) yields

$$T_1 = 2\pi/\omega(a - qn)^{1/2} = T/(a - qn)^{1/2} \qquad (8.5.1)$$

where $q = -r$ and $a = 1 - r$. If not all units interact with each other, then this equation will be valid for $n < n_0$, where n_0 is the number of directly coupled oscillators. For $n > n_0$, T_1 will be approximately constant. The exact expressions for this case are very cumbersome, but one can see that similar results are obtained in the case of a continuum of oscillators. Figure 8.5.1 shows the plot of T_1 versus n while Fig. 8.5.2 shows the results obtained in Jacklet's experiments.

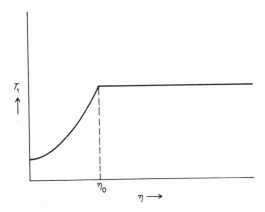

FIG. 8.5.1. Dependence of the period on the size of population of interacting oscillators n where n_0 is the size of the pool of directly interacting units.

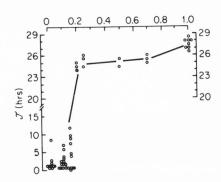

FIG. 8.5.2. Period of oscillations as a function of size [Jac-3].

8.6 Synchronization of Populations of Light-Emitting Organisms

Synchronization among various biological oscillators can occur even
when the coupling is not direct but through sensory organs. Examples
of this phenomenon are offered by organisms which emit light flashes
in a periodic manner [Han-1]. In many cases such organisms can be
entrained by light cycles and thus are subject to entrainment by the
light emitted by other individuals. It is not surprising that mutual
entrainment can be observed.

A mathematical model of such a population could be described most
conveniently through phase response curves (PRC's). Let $p(\theta)$ be the
amount of phase shift caused on an individual when exposed to a flash
of light at phase θ. Let zero be the phase at which an individual emits

a flash. Let $\theta_i(t)$ denote the phase as a function of time of the ith individual (Fig. 8.6.1a). Figure 8.6.1b shows a possible PRC. A superposition of this curve and $\theta_i(t)$ can determine the changes caused by light pulses in $\theta_i(t)$ (Fig. 8.6.1c).

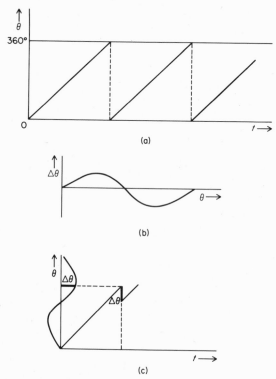

(a)

(b)

(c)

FIG. 8.6.1.   (a) Plot of phase versus time in the absence of perturbations; (b) PRC; (c) effect of disturbances on the phase-time plot.

For simplicity we study the interaction of only two units. Initially we assume that one unit (#1) is ahead of the other (#2) by phase σ so that

$$\Delta\theta = \sigma \tag{8.6.1}$$

After the first pulse is emitted (by unit #1) unit #2 is phase shifted by $p(\tau - \sigma)$, where $p(\theta)$ is the PRC and τ the period. Hence

$$\Delta\theta = \sigma - p(\tau - \sigma) \tag{8.6.2}$$

If unit #2 flashes next unit #1 is phase shifted by $p[\sigma - p(\tau - \sigma)]$ so that

$$\Delta\theta = \sigma - p(\tau - \sigma) + p[\sigma - p(\tau - \sigma)] \tag{8.6.3}$$

and so forth. In general, if the phase difference between unit 1 and 2 is $\Delta\theta_n$ after unit #2 has flashed, then following the next flash of unit #1 we have

$$\Delta\theta_{n+1} = \Delta\theta_n - p(\tau - \Delta\theta_n) \qquad (8.6.4)$$

and, after the next flash of unit #2,

$$\Delta\theta_{n+2} = \Delta\theta_{n+1} + p(\Delta\theta_{n+1}) \qquad (8.6.5)$$

Thus we have a recursive relation of the type studied in Section 4.5. Both equations must be interpreted modulo τ. Figure 8.6.2 illustrates

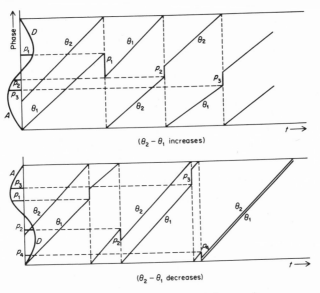

FIG. 8.6.2.   Mutual entrainment of two units.

this sequence of events for two different PRC's. A necessary condition for entrainment is that the time between flashes be constant, i.e., if $\Delta\theta_n = $ const. This can happen if and only if

$$p(\Delta\theta) = p(\tau - \Delta\theta) = 0 \qquad (8.6.6)$$

where $\Delta\theta$ is the fixed phase. The stability of entrainment will be studied in the same manner as in Section 4.5. We have

$$\frac{d(\Delta\theta_{n+1})}{d(\Delta\theta_n)} = 1 - \frac{dp(\tau - \Delta\theta_n)}{d(\Delta\theta_n)} \qquad (8.6.7)$$

and

$$\frac{d(\Delta\theta_{n+2})}{d(\Delta\theta_{n+1})} = 1 + \frac{dp(\Delta\theta_{n+1})}{d(\Delta\theta_{n+1})} \tag{8.6.8}$$

Equations (8.6.6)–(8.6.8), together with the condition for stability (4.5.13), give

$$\left| 1 - \frac{dp(\tau - x)}{dx} \right| \left| 1 + \frac{dp(x)}{dx} \right| < 1 \qquad \text{for} \quad x = \Delta\theta \tag{8.6.9}$$

As we have seen in Chapter 3, most PRC's have only two zeros and Eq. (8.6.6) requires that their sum be τ (or zero). The derivatives of $p(x)$ on each one will have opposite signs because of the periodicity of PRC's (a discontinuity counts as a zero). If their absolute values do not exceed 2 and they are of comparable size, then Eq. (8.6.9) can be interpreted as requiring

$$dp/dx < 0 \qquad \text{at} \quad x = \Delta\theta \tag{8.6.10}$$

Thus in Fig. 8.6.2 the second curve gives stable entrainment for $\Delta\theta = 0$ while the first does so for $\Delta\theta = T/2$. The first corresponds to synchronous flashing while the second to flashing 180° apart (compare Sections 7.6, 8.2, and 8.3).

These results can be generalized easily for more oscillators. In particular a necessary and sufficient condition for flashing in synchrony is that the PRC have a zero for $\theta = 0$ with negative derivative.

Entrainment by external pulse trains has verified the properties of pulse entrainment discussed in Section 4.5. Phase advances are observed if the external period T_1 exceeds that of the endogenous oscillations T and phase delays are seen when $T_1 < T$.

In one set of experiments fireflies which present a free-run rhythm with period of 980 msec were entrained successfully by light-pulse trains of 1136 and 838 msec, as well as 980 msec. In the first case the light pulse occurs 203 msec before the flash (which corresponds to phase zero). In the second, 192 msec after the flash, and in the third simultaneously with the flash [Han-1].

According to the theory of Section 4.5 succesful entrainment implies a phase shift at the time of application of the light pulse equal to the difference in the periods; i.e.,

$$\Delta\phi_1 = 1136 - 980 = 156 \quad \text{msec}$$
$$\Delta\phi_2 = 838 - 980 = -142 \quad \text{msec}$$
$$\Delta\phi_3 = 0$$

The phase of the oscillators must be such that these phase shifts be obtained from the PRC when the light pulse occurs. Therefore the observed relations between flashes and light pulses give us three points of the PRC, as shown in Fig. 8.6.3. The limits of entrainment were

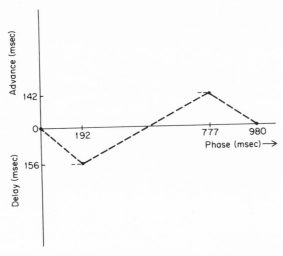

FIG. 8.6.3.   Inferred phase response curve for the flashing rhythm of fireflies.

found to be close to the above periods. Thus it would not be surprising if these points are the extrema of the PRC. This shape of the PRC conforms to the prediction of the analysis on the basis of recursive relations.

8.7   Nonmonotonic Period Transients

It has been observed that following a chance in environmental conditions the free-run period of circadian activity reaches its steady-state value only after long transients [Esk-1, Esk-2, Pit-9]. Quite often these are not monotonic. For example, an increase in period is followed by a decrease and then another increase, etc. [Esk-1, Esk-2, Pit-9].

Oscillators with one degree of freedom of the type described in Section 1.5 do not exhibit such behavior. Since their oscillations are isoperiodic, the period of oscillations will be roughly the same outside the limit cycle as on it. Thus after a parameter change the period will reach its new value quickly, long before the state of the system arrives at the steady-state trajectory (Fig. 8.7.1). Of course one could construct other models with more complex structure to simulate the phenomenon,

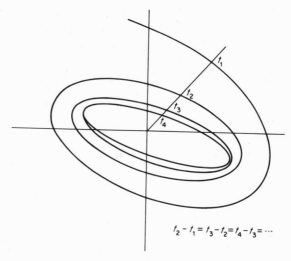

FIG. 8.7.1.   Phase plane portrait of a trajectory approaching a limit cycle L. If the oscillations are isoperiodic, then $t_2 - t_1 = t_3 - t_2 = t_4 - t_3 = \cdots$.

but this would require overspecification in order to give even a qualitative description of the phenomenon.

A simpler solution is offered by populations of oscillators. Although a complete analysis of the phenomenon is lacking, the following simple argument shows why this will be so.

Consider two oscillators with frequencies ω_1 and ω_2 which are weakly coupled and can be mutually entrained but with long transients. The behavior of the system is controlled by the sum of their outputs. Whenever the latter exceeds a threshold T activity starts. A gross simplification of such a system can be given by assuming their outputs sinosoidal so that

$$y(t) = \sin \omega_1 t + \sin \omega_2 t \qquad (8.7.1)$$

and that $|\omega_1 - \omega_2|$ tends to zero as time increases. Equation (8.7.1) can be written as

$$y(t) = 2 \sin \left(\frac{\omega_1 + \omega_2}{2} t \right) \cdot \cos \left(\frac{\omega_1 - \omega_2}{2} t \right) \qquad (8.7.2)$$

which is an oscillation with beats.

Suppose now that during a change in the environment a change in parameters occurs, but each oscillator responds with a different speed.

Again a simplified model will be to set

$$\omega_1 = \omega_{new} + e^{-t/T_1}(\omega_{old} - \omega_{new}) \tag{8.7.3a}$$

$$\omega_2 = \omega_{new} + e^{-t/T_2}(\omega_{old} - \omega_{new}) \tag{8.7.3b}$$

Equations (8.7.2) and (8.7.3) were simulated on a computer through a FORTRAN program using $T_1 = 20$, $T_2 = 100$, $\omega_{old} = 1$, and $\omega_{new} = 2$. The crossings (from smaller to larger) of $y(t)$ with a threshold equal to 0.2 were taken as timing events. Figure 8.7.2 shows

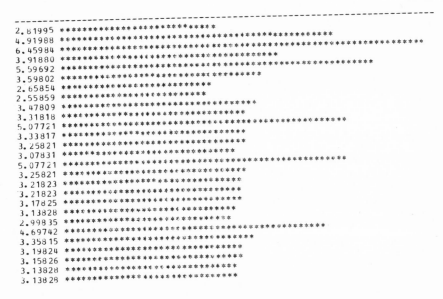

FIG. 8.7.2. Change of the period of oscillations as a function of time as measured by the time intervals between successive events (see text).

the results. The numbers on the bottom equal the time interval between two successive events while the lines of asterisks were plotted in proportion to the period. This is qualitatively similar to Fig. 8.2.1 (D–F) and other experimental results ([Esk-2, Figs. 5–7]).

This is one possible explanation of the long and nonmonotonic transients which can be described as a temporary loss of synchrony among the various units which results in frequency beats modulating the free-run period.

Recently C. Berde conducted a study of nonmonotonic transients as part of a Swarthmore College senior thesis. He verified by computer simulation that the model of Sec. 8.3 indeed presents such transients provided that the units are weakly coupled and the units are not identical.

8.8   Bibliographical Notes

There is no limit in the number of biological phenomena which are attributable to properties of coupled oscillators. As we have seen in the previous chapter, many studies of populations of oscillators have been done within the framework of biology [Goo-A, Win-0, Pav-8, Pav-11, Pav-12, etc.]. Examples of particular systems have been referenced in the individual sections. A series of relevant studies have been made by Prigogine and his co-workers [Ede-1, Lav-1, Lef-1, Lef-2, Lef-3, Pri-1, Pri-4, Pri-5, Pri-6] regarding chemical oscillations in both time and space. Other investigators have reported on models of biochemical wave propagation in a biological medium [Goo-1, Win-6]. The zonation patterns in fungi cultures can be considered as a special case of stationary waves. For more interesting speculations on the role of biochemical waves, the reader is referred to the work of Goodwin and Cohen [Goo-1]. Needless to say, the study of populations of oscillators has bearing in insect or cellular populations [Edm-6, Han-1].

References

Each reference in this monograph is described by the first three letters (or more if ambiquity arises) of the author or the first author followed by an ordinal to distinguish among works by the same author.

Roman numerals are used as ordinals for books on the Mathematical Theory of Oscillators, capital letters for books on Biological Oscillations, and arabic numerals for papers.

At each reference the number of the sections of the text where it is mentioned is indicated in brackets.

Books on the Mathematical Theory of Oscillators

Aiz-I   Aizerman, M. A., and F. R. Gantmacher, *Absolute Stability of Regulator Systems.* Holden-Day, San Francisco, California, 1964 [7.8].

And-I   Andronov, A. A., A. A. Vitt, and S. E. Khaikin, *Theory of Oscillators.* Pergamon, Oxford. U.S. Edition: Addison-Wesley, Reading, Massachusetts, 1966 [1.1, 1.2, 1.7, 4.5, 5.3, 7.2, 7.8].

Bel-I   Bellman, R., *Methods of Nonlinear Analysis*, Vol. 1. Academic Press, New York, 1970 [1.5].

Bes-I   Besicovitch, A. S., *Almost Periodic Functions.* Dover, New York, 1954 [1.4].

Bog-I   Bogoliubov, N. N., and Y. A. Mitropolsky, *Asymptotic Methods in the Theory of Non-Linear Oscillations.* Hindustan Publ. Corp., Delhi, 1961 [1.1, 1.5, 7.2, 7.3, 7.8].

But-I   Butenin, N. V., *Elements of the Theory of Nonlinear Oscillations.* Ginn (Blaisdell), Boston, Massachusetts, 1965 [1.1, 4.2, 4.8, 4.7].

Chu-I   Churchill, R. V., *Fourier Series and Boundary Value Problems.* McGraw-Hill, New York, 1941 [8.4].

Dav-I   Davies, T. V., and E. M. James, *Nonlinear Differential Equations.* Addison-Wesley, Reading, Massachusetts, 1966 [1.1].

Fes-I   Feshchenko, S. F., N. I. Shkil, and L. D. Mikolenko, *Asymptotic Methods in the Theory of Linear Differential Equations.* Amer. Elsevier, New York, 1967 [1.5].

187

Gel-I   Gelb, A., and W. E. Vander Velde, *Multiple-Input Describing Functions and Nonlinear System Design*. McGraw-Hill, New York, 1968   [1.6].

Gib-I   Gibson, J. E., *Nonlinear Automatic Control*. McGraw-Hill, New York, 1963 [1.6].

Haa-I   Haag, J., *Oscillatory Motions*. Wadsworth, Belmont, California, 1962   [1.1, 4.2, 4.7].

Haj-I   Hajeck, O., *Dynamical Systems in the Plane*. Academic Press, New York, 1968 [1.1].

Hal-I   Hale, J. K., *Oscillations in Nonlinear Systems*. McGraw-Hill, New York, 1963 [1.1].

Hay-I   Hayashi, C., *Nonlinear Oscillations in Physical Systems*. McGraw-Hill, New York, 1964   [1.1, 4.7].

Jur-I   Jury, E.I., *Theory and Application of the z-Ttransform Method*. Wiley, New York, 1964   [4.5].

LaS-I   LaSalle, J., and S. Lefschetz, *Stability by Liapunov's Direct Method with Applications*. Academic Press, New York, 1961   [1.4].

Lef-I   Lefschetz, S., *Differential Equations: Geometric Theory*, 2nd ed. Wiley (Interscience), New York, 1962   [1.1].

Lef-II   Lefschetz, S., *Stability of Nonlinear Control Systems*. Academic Press, New York, 1965   [1.1].

Lev-I   Levy, H., and F. Lessman, *Finite Difference Equations*. Macmillan, New York, 1961   [4.5].

Mal-I   Malkin, I. G., *Some Problems in the Theory of Nonlinear Oscillations*, Books 1 and 2, AEC-tr-3766. U.S. At. Energy Comm., Washington, D.C., 1959 (Russian original 1956)   [1.5].

Min-I   Minorsky, N., *Nonlinear Oscillations*. Van Nostrand-Reinhold, Princeton, New Jersey, 1962   [1.1, 1.2, 1.5, 1.7, 4.2, 4.7].

Min-II   Minorsky, N., *Theory of Nonlinear Control Systems*. McGraw-Hill, New York, 1969   [1.1].

Mit-I   Mitropolski, Yu. A., *Problems of the Asymptotic Theory of Nonstationary Vibrations*. Israel Program for Sci. Transl., Jerusalem, 1965   [1.5].

Nem-I   Nemytskii, V. V., and V. V. Stepanov, *Qualitative Theory of Differential Equations*. Princeton Univ. Press, Princeton, New Jersey, 1960   [1.1].

Oga-I   Ogata, K., *State Space Analysis of Control Systems*. Prentice-Hall, Englewood Cliffs, New Jersey, 1967   [1.1, 1.4, 6.2].

Oga-II   Ogata, K., *Modern Control Engineering*. Prentice-Hall, Englewood Cliffs, New Jersey, 1970   [1.1, 1.2, 1.4, 1.6].

Pli-I   Pliss, V. A., *Nonlocal Problems of the Theory of Oscillations*. Academic Press, New York, 1966   [1.1].

Saa-I   Saaty, T. L., *Modern Nonlinear Equations*. McGraw Hill, New York, 1967 [1.1].

San-I   Sansone, G., and R. Conti, *Nonlinear Differential Equations*. Macmillan, New York, 1964   [1.1, 4.7].

Ura-I   Urabe, M., *Nonlinear Autonomous Oscillations*. Academic Press, New York, 1967   [1.1, 1.7].

Zad-I   Zadeh, L. A., and C. A. Desoer, *Linear System Theory*. McGraw-Hill, New York, 1963   [1.4, 6.2].

Zub-I   Zubov, V. I., *Methods of A.M. Lyapunov and Their Application*. Noordhoff, Groningen, 1964   [1.4].

Books on Biological Oscillators (Including Collections of Papers)

Asc-A   Aschoff, J., ed., *Proc. Feldafing Summer School, September* 1964 *Circadian Clocks.* North-Holland Publ., Amsterdam, 1965 [2.2].

Bro-A   Brown, F. A., S. W. Hastings, and J. D. Palmer, *The Biological Clock: Two Views.* Academic Press, New York, 1970 [2.2].

Bün-A   Bünning, E., *The Physiological Clock.* Springer-Verlag, Berlin and New York, 1967 [2.2, 4.3].

Cha-A   Chance, B., E. K. Pye, B. Hess, and A. Ghosh, ed. *Biological and Biochemical Oscillators,* Academic Press, 1973 [2.5].

Col-A   *Cold Spring Harbor Symp. Quantitative Biol.,* 1960, *Biological Clocks.* 25 [2.2].

Fra-A   Frank, G. M., *et al.,* eds., *Oscillatory Processes in Biological and Chemical Systems.* Nauka, Moscow, 1967 (in Russian) [2.5].

Ger-A   Gerstenhaber, M., ed., *Some Mathematical Problems in Biology.* Amer. Math Soc., Providence, Rhode Island, 1968 [1.3].

Ger-B   Gerstenhaber, M., ed., *Some Mathematical Questions in Biology.* Amer. Math. Soc., Providence, Rhode Island, 1970 [1.3].

Goe-A   Goel, N. S., S. C. Maitra, and E. W. Montrolli, *On the Volterra and Other Nonlinear Models of Interacting Populations.* Academic Press, New York, 1971 [1.3].

Goo-A   Goodwin, B. C., *Temporal Organization in Cells.* Academic Press, New York, 1963 [7.8, 8.8].

Har-A   Harker, J. E., *The Physiology of Diurnal Rhythms.* Cambridge Univ. Press, London and New York, 1964 [2.2, 8.1].

Lot-A   Lotka, A. J., *Elements of Mathematical Biology.* Dover, New York, 1956 (republication of 1st ed. of 1924) [1.3].

Luc-A   Luce, G. G., *Biological Rhythms in Human & Animal Physiology.* Dover, New York, 1971 [2.2].

Mac-A   MacArthur, R. H., and E. O. Wilson, *Island Biogeography.* Princeton Univ. Press, Princeton, New Jersey, 1967 [1.3].

Mar-A   Marois, M., ed., *Theoretical Physics and Biology.* North-Holland Publ., Amsterdam, 1969.

May-A   Maynard Smith, J., *Mathematical Ideas in Biology.* Cambridge Univ. Press, London and New York, 1968 [1.3].

Men-A   Menaker, M., *Proc. Symp. Friday Harbor, Washington, September* 1969, *Biochronometry.* Nat. Acad. Sci., Washington, D. C., 1971 [2.2].

Pie-A   Pielou, E. C., *An Introduction to Mathematical Ecology.* Wiley (Interscience), New York, 1969 [1.3].

Rei-A   Reiss, R. F., *Neural Theory and Modeling.* Stanford Univ. Press, Stanford, California, 1964 [2.6].

Ros-A   Rosen, R., *Dynamical System Theory in Biology.* Wiley (Interscience), New York, 1970 [6.2].

Sol-A   Sollberger, A., *Biological Rhythm Research.* Elsevier, Amsterdam, 1965 [2.2].

Sta-A   Stark, L., *Neurological Control Systems.* Plenum, New York, 1968 [2.6].

Swe-A   Sweeney, B. M., *Rhythmic Phenomena in Plants.* Academic Press, New York, 1969 [2.2].

Vol-A   Volterra, V., *Theorie Mathematique de la lutte pour la vie.* Gauthier-Villars, Paris, 1931 [1.3].

vonM-A   von Mayersbach, H., ed., The *Cellular Aspects of Biorythms.* Springer-Verlag, Berlin and New York, 1967 [2.4].

Wat-A   Waterman, T. H., and H. J. Morowitz, eds., *Theoretical and Mathematical Biology.* Ginn (Blaisdell), Boston, Massachusetts, 1965

Wit-A   Withrow, R. B., ed., *Photoperiodism and Related Phenomena in Plants and Animals.* Amer. Assoc. Advan. Sci., Washington, D.C., 1959   [2.2, 4.8].

Zeu-A   Zeuthen, E., ed., *Synchrony in Cell Division and Growth.* Wiley (Interscience), New York, 1964   [2.4].

Papers

Adk-1   Adkisson, P. L., "Light-Dark Reactions Involved in Insect Diapause," *Proc. Feldafing Summer School, September 1964, Circadian Clocks,* pp. 344–350. North-Holland Publ., Amsterdam, 1965   [4.8].

Adk-2   Adkisson, P. L., and S. H. Roach, "A Mechanism for Seasonal Discrimination in the Photoperiodic Induction of Pupal Diapause in the Bollworm *Heliothis zea* (Bodelie)." *Proc. Symp., Friday Harbor, Washington, September 1969, Biochronometry,* pp. 272–280. Nat. Acad. Sci., Washington, D.C., 1971   [4.8].

Adl-1   Adler, K., "Extraoptic Phase Shifting of Circadian Locomotor Rhythm in Salamanders." *Science* **164**, 1290–1292. (1969)   [6.6].

Adl-2   Adler, K., "Pineal End Organ: Role in Extraoptic Entrainment of Circadian Locomotor Rhythm in Frogs." *Proc. Symp., Friday Harbor, Washington, September 1969, Biochronometry,* pp. 342–350. Nat. Acad. Sci., Washington, D.C., 1971   [6.6].

Agg-1   Aggarwal, J. K., and C. G. Richie, "On Coupled van der Pol Oscillators." *IEEE Trans. Circuit Theory* **CT-13**, 465–466 (1966)   [7.8].

Agg-2   Aggarwal, J. K., and H. H. Bybee, "On Coupled Systems." *IEEE Trans. Circuit Theory* **CT-17**, 141–144 (1970)   [7.8].

Arv-1   Arvanitaki, N., and N. Chalazonitis, "Electrical properties and Temporal Organization in Oscillatory Neurons (Aplysia)." *Symp. Neurobiol. of Invertebrates* (J. Salanki, ed.), pp. 169–199. Plenum, New York, 1968   [2.6].

Asc-1   Aschoff, J., "Exogenous and Endogenous Components in Circadian Rhythms." *Cold Spring Harbor Symp. Quantitative Biol.,* 1960, *Biological Clocks,* **25**, pp. 11–27 Cold Spring Harbor Lab. Quant. Biol., Cold Spring Harbor, New York   [2.2, 4.8, 5.3].

Asc-2   Aschoff, J., "Response Curves in Circadian Periodicity." *Proc. Feldafing Summer School, September 1964, Circadian Clocks,* pp. 95–111. North-Holland Publ., Amsterdam, 1965   [2.2, 3.7, 6.2].

Asc-3   Aschoff, J., "The Phase-Angle Difference in Circadian Periodicity." *Proc. Feldafing Summer School, September 1964, Circadian Clocks,* pp. 262–276. North-Holland Publ., Amsterdam, 1965   [4.8].

Asc-4   Aschoff, J., "Circadian Rhythms in Man." *Science* **148**, 1427–1432 (1965)   [2.2].

Asc-5   Aschoff, J., "Circadian Activity Pattern with Two Peaks." *Ecology* **47**, 657–662 (1966)   [8.2].

Asc-6   Aschoff, J., "Minimal Heat Conductance of Man During Night and Day." *Pflugers Arch. Gesamte Physiol. Menschen Tiere* **295**, 184–196 (1967)   [2.2].

Asc-7   Aschoff, J., V. Gerecke, and R. Wever, "Phase Relationships Between the Circadian Periods of Activity and the Internal Temperature of Man." *Pflügers Arch. Gesamte Physiol. Menschen Tiere* **295**, 173–183 (1968)   [2.2, 8.2].

Asc-8   Aschoff, J., V. V. Saint Paul, and R. Wever, "Circadian Period of Finches as

Influenced by Self-Selected Light–Dark Cycles," *Z. Vergl. Physiol.* **58**, 304–321 (1968) (in German) [2.2].

Asc-9 Aschoff, J., "Phasing of Diurnal Rhythms as a Function of Season and Latitude," *Oecologia* **3**, 125–165 (1969) (in German) [4.8].

Asc-10 Aschoff, J., E. Poppel, and R. Wever, "Circadian Rhythms in Men as Influenced by Artificial Light–Dark Cycles of Various Period," *Pflügers Arch. Physiol.* **306**, 58–70 (1969) (in German) [2.2, 2.4, 8.2].

Asc-11 Aschoff, J. *et al.*, "Independent Parameters of Circadian Activity Rhythms in Birds and Man," *Proc. Symp., Friday Harbor, Washington, September 1969, Biochronometry*, pp. 3–29. Nat. Acad. Sci., Washington, D. C., 1971 [5.7].

Asc-12 Aschoff, J. *et al.*, "Human Circadian Rhythms in Continuous Darkness: Entrainment by Social Cues," *Science* **71**, 213–215 (1971) [2.2].

Bar-1 Barlow, J. S., "A Phase Comparator Model for the Diurnal Rhythm of Emergence of *Drosophila*," *Am. New York Acad. Sciences* **98**, 788–805 (1962) [5.7].

Barn-1 Barnett, A., C. F. Ehret and J. J. Wille, Jr., "Testing the Chronon Theory of Circadian Timekeeping," *Proc. Symp., Friday Harbor, Washington, September 1969, Biochronometry*, pp. 637–651. Nat. Acad. Sci., Washington, D. C., 1971 [5.7].

Bel-1 Beljostina, L. N. and G. A. Kokina, "Qualitative Investigation of Systems of Equations of Photosynthesis," *Oscill. Proc. Biol. Chem. Systems* (A. M. Frank *et al.*, ed) 67–80. (in Russian) [2.5].

Bet-1 Betz, A. and B. Chance, "Influence of Inhibitors and Temperature on the Oscillation of Reduced Pyridine Nucleotides in Yeast Cells," *Arch. Biochem. Biophys.* **109**, 579–584 (1965) [2.5].

Bet-2 Betz, A. and B. Chance, "Phase Relationships of Glycolytic Intermediates in Yeast Cells with Oscillatory Metabolic Control," *Arch. Biochem. Biophys.* **109**, 585–594 (1965) [2.5].

Bin-1 Binkley, S., E. Kluth, M. Menaker, "Pineal Function in Sparrows: Circadian Rhythms and Body Temperature," *Science* **184**, 311–314 (1971) [6.6].

Boum-1 Bouma, H., and L. C. J. Baghuis, "Hippus of the Pupil: Periods of Slow Oscillations of Unknown Origin." *Vision Res.* **11**, 1345–1351 (1971) [2.6].

Bour-1 Bourret, J. A., R. G. Lincoln, and R. H. Carpenter, "Fungal Endogenous Rhythms Expressed by Spiral Figures." *Science* **166**, 763–764 (1969) [2.7, 8.4].

Bra-1 Brady, J., "Control of the Circadian Rhythm of Activity in the Cockroach: I. The Role of the Corpora Cardiaca Brain and Stress." *J. Exp. Biol.* **47**, 153–163 (1967) [6.6].

Bra-2 Brady, J., "Control of the Circadian Rhythm of Activity in the Cockroach. II. The Role of the Sub-œsophageal Ganglion Ant Ventral Nerve Cord." *J. Exp. Biol.* **47**, 165-178 (1967) [6.6].

Bra-3 Brady, J., "The Search for an Insect Clock." *Proc. Symp., Friday Harbor, Washington, September 1969, Biochronometry*, pp. 517–526. Nat. Acad. Sci., Washington, D.C., 1971 [6.6].

Bri-1 Brinkmann, K., "Temperatureinflüsse auf die Circadiane Rhythmik von Euglane gracilis bei Mixotrophie und Autotrophie." *Planta* **70**, 344–389 (1966) [2.4, 6.4].

Bri-2 Brinkmann, K., "Metabolic Control of Temperature Compensation in the Circadian Rhythm of *Euglena gracilis*." *Proc. Symp., Friday Harbor, Washington, September 1969, Biochronometry*, pp. 567–593. Nat. Acad. Sci., Washington, D.C., 1971 [2.4, 6.4].

Bru-1 Bruce, V. G., and C. S. Pittendrigh, "An Effect of Heavy Water on the Phase and Period of the Circadian Rhythm in *Euglena*." *J. Cell. Comp. Physiol.* **56**, 25–31 (1960) [6.5].

Bru-2   Bruce, V. G., "Environmental Entrainment of Circadian Rhythms." *Cold Spring Harbor Sypm. Quantitative Biol.*, 1960, *Biological Clocks*, **25**, pp. 29–48. Cold Spring Harbor Lab. Quant. Biol., Cold Spring Harbor, New York [4.8].

Bru-3   Bruce, V. G., "Cell Division Rhythms and the Circadian Clock." *Proc. Feldafing Summer School, September* 1964, *Circadian Clocks*, pp. 125–138. North-Holland Publ., Amsterdam, 1965   [2.4].

Bru-4   Bruce, V. G., "The Biological Clock in *Chlamydomonas reinhardi*." *J. Protozool.* **17**, 328–334 (1970)   [2.4].

Bru-5   Bruce, V. G., "Mutants of the Biological Clock in Chlamydomonas Reinhardi," *Genetics* **70**, 537–548 (1972)   [2.2].

Bün-1   Bünning, E., "Opening Address: Biological Clocks." *Cold Spring Harbor Symp. Quantitative Biol.*, 1960, *Biological Clocks*, **25**, pp. 1–9. Cold Spring Harbor Lab. Quant. Biol., Cold Spring Harbor, New York   [2.2].

Bün-2   Bünning, E., "Circadian Rhythms and the Time Measurement in Photoperiodism." *Cold Spring Harbor Symp. Quantitative Biol.*, 1960, *Biological Clocks*, **25**, pp. 249–256. Cold Spring Harbor Lab. Quant. Biol., Cold Spring Harbor, New York   [4.8].

Bün-3   Bünning, E., and I. Moser, "Response Kurven bei der Circadienen Rhythmik von *Phaseolus*." *Planta* **69**, 101–110 (1966)   [5.2].

Bün-4   Bünning, E., "The Adaptive Value of Circadian Leaf Movements." *Proc. Symp., Friday Harbor, Washington, September* 1969, *Biochronometry*, pp. 203–211. Nat. Acad. Sci., Washington, D. C.,1971   [2.2].

Bus-1   Busse, H. G., "A Spatial Periodic Homogeneous Chemical Reaction." *J. Phys. Chem.* **73**, 750 (1969)   [2.5, 8.4].

Cai-1   Cain, T. R., and W. O. Wilson, "A Test of the Circadian Rule of Aschoff with Chicken Hens." *J. Interdiscipl. Cycle Res.* **3**, 77–85 (1972)   [5.2].

Chal-1   Chalazonitis, N., "Synaptic Properties of Oscillatory Neurons (Aplysia and Helix)." *Symp. on Neurobiol. Invertebrates* (J. Salanki, ed.), pp. 201–224. Plenum, New York (1968)   [2.6].

Cha-1   Chance, B., B. Schuener, and S. Elsaessar, "Control of the Waveform of Oscillations of the Reduced Pyridine Nucleotide Level in a Cell-Free Extract." *Proc. Nat. Acad. Sci. U.S.* **52**, 337–341 (1964)   [2.5].

Cha-2   Chance, B., and T. Yoshioka, "Sustained Oscillations of Ionic Constituents of Mitochondria." *Arch. Bioch. Biophys.* **117**, 451–465 (1966)   [2.5].

Cha-3   Chance, B., K. Pye, and J. Higgins, "Waveform Generation by Enzymatic Oscillators." *IEEE Spectrum* **4**, 79–86 (1967)   [2.5].

Chan-1   Chandrasekaran, M. K., and W. Loher, "The Effect of Light Intensity on the Circadian Rhythms of Eclosion in *Drosophila pseuobscura*." *Z. Vergl. Physiol.* **62**, 337–347 (1969)   [2.3].

Com-1   Comorosan, S., "New Mechanism for the Control of Cellular Reactions: the Biochemical Flip-Flop." *Nature* (London) **227**, 64–65 (1970)   [2.5].

Dea-1   Deamer, D. W., K. Utsumi, and L. Packer, "Oscillatory States of Mitochondria. III. Ultrastructure of Trapped Conformation States." *Arch. Biochem. Biophys.* **121**, 641–651 (1967)   [2.5].

DeC-1   DeCoursey, P. J., "Phase Control of Activity in a Rodent." *Cold Spring Harbor Symp. Quantitative Biol.*, 1960, *Biological Clocks*, **25**, pp. 49–55. Cold Spring Harbor Lab. Quant. Biol., Cold Spring Harbor, New York   [3.7].

DeC-2   DeCoursey, P. J., "Daily Light Sensitivity Rhythm in a Rodent." *Science* 131, 33–35 (1960)   [2.2, 3.3, 3.7].

DeC-3   DeCoursey, P. J., "Effect of Light on the Circadian Activity Rhythm of the Flying Squirrel *Glaucomys volans*." *Z. Vergl. Physiol.* 44, 331–354 (1961) [3.7].

Dun-1   Dunin-Barkovsky, V. L., "Some Properties of the Group of Neurons Working in Parallel. I. Neuron Pool without Interconnections." *Biofizika* 16, 520–525 (1971) (in Russian)   [2.6].

Dun-2   Dunin-Barkovsky, V. L., "Some Properties of a Group of Neurons Working in Parallel. II. Role of Inhibitory and Excitatory Connections Between Neurons." *Biofizika* 16, 700–706 (1971) (in Russian)   [2.6].

Dun-3   Dunin-Barkovsky, V. L., "On the Stability of Activity Level in a Net of Excitable Elements." *Biofizika* 16, 911–914 (1971) (in Russian)   [2.6, 7.8].

Dun-4   Dunin-Barkovsky, V. L., and V. S. Jacobson, "Analysis of Transient Processes and Oscillation in a Net of Neuron-Counters." *Biofizika* 16, 1080–1084 (1971) (in Russian)   [2.6, 7.8].

Ede-1   Edelstein, B. B., "Biochemical Model with Multiple Steady States and Hysteresis." *J. Theor. Biol.* 29, 57–62 (1970)   [2.5, 8.8].

Edm-1   Edmunds, L. N., Jr., "Studies on Synchronously Dividing Cultures of *Euglena gracilis* Klebs (Strain Z). I. Attainment and Characterization of Rhythmic Cell Division." *J. Cell. Comp. Physiol.* 66, 147–158 (1965)   [2.4].

Edm-2   Edmunds, L. N., Jr., "Studies on Synchronously Dividing Cultures of *Euglena gracilis* Klebs (Strain Z). II. Patterns of Biosynthesis During the Cell Cycle." *J. Cell. Comp. Physiol.* 66, 159–182 (1965)   [2.4].

Edm-3   Edmunds, L. N., Jr., "Studies on Synchronously Dividing Cultures of *Euglena gracilis* Klebs (Strain Z). III. Circadian Components of Cell Division." *J. Cell. Comp. Physiol.* 67, 35–44 (1966)   [2.4].

Edm-4   Edmunds, L. N., Jr., and R. R. Funch, "Circadian Rhythm of Cell Division in *Euglena*: Effects of a Random Illumination Regimen." *Science* 165, 500–503 (1969)   [2.4].

Edm-5   Edmunds, L. N., Jr., and R. Funch, "Effects of 'Skeleton' Photoperiods and High Frequency Light-Dark Cycles on the Rhythm of Cell Division in Synchronized Cultures of *Euglena*." *Planta* 87, 134–163 (1969)   [2.4, 4.6].

Edm-6   Edmunds, L. N., Jr., "Persistent Circadian Rhythm of Cell Division in *Euglena*: Some Theoretical Considerations and the Problem of Intercellular Communication." *Proc. Symp., Friday Harbor, Washington, September* 1969, *Biochronometry*, pp. 594–611. Nat. Acad. Sci., Washington, D.C., 1971   [2.4, 8.8].

Ehr-1   Ehret, C. F., and J. S. Barlow, "Toward a Realistic Model of a Biological Period Measuring Mechanism." *Cold Spring Harbor Symp. Quantitative Biol.,* 1960, *Biological Clocks,* 25, pp. 217–220. Cold Spring Harbor Lab. Quant. Biol., Cold Spring Harbor, New York   [5.7].

Ehr-2   Ehret, C. F., and E. Trucco, "Molecular Models for the Circadian Clock. I. The Chronon Concept." *J. Theor. Biol.* 15, 240–262 (1967)   [5.7].

Enr-1   Enright, J. T., "Synchronization and Ranges of Entrainment." *Proc. Feldafing Summer School, September* 1964, *Circadian Clocks,* pp. 112–124. North-Holland Publ., Amsterdam, 1965   [4.8].

Enr-2   Enright, J. T., "The Search for Rhythmicity in Biological Time-Series." *J. Theor. Biol.* 8, 426–468 (1965)   [5.7].

Enr-3   Enright, J. T., "Heavy Water Slows Biological Timing Process." *Z. Vergl. Physiol.* 72, 1–16 (1971)   [6.5].

Enr-4   Enright, J. T., "The Internal Clock of Drunken Isopods." *Z. Vergl. Physiol.* **75**, 332–346 (1971)   [6.5].

Erk-1   Erkert, H., "Beleuchtungsabhängige Aktivitätsoptima bei Eulen und Circadiane Regel." *Naturwissenschaften* **54**, 231–232 (1967)   [5.2].

Esk-1   Eskin, A., "The Sparrow Clock: Behavior of the Free Running Rhythm and Entrainment Analysis." *Ph.D. Thesis,* Dept. of Zoology, Univ. of Texas, Austin, 1969   [5.2, 8.7].

Esk-2   Eskin, A., "Some Properties of the System Controlling the Circadian Activity Rhythm of Sparrows." *Proc. Symp., Friday Harbor, Washington, September* 1969, *Biochronometry,* pp. 55–80. Nat. Acad. Sci., Washington, D.C., 1971   [8.7].

Esk-3   Eskin, A., "Properties of the *Aplysia* Visual System: In Vitro Entrainment of the Circadian Rhythm and Centrifugal Regulation of the Eye." *Z. Vergl. Physiol.* **74**, 353–371 (1971)   [4.8].

Esk-4   Eskin, A., "Phase Shifting a Circadian Rhythm in the Eye of *Aplysia* by Depolarizing High Potassium Pulses." *J. Comp. Physiol.* **80**, 353–376 (1972)   [6.6].

Far-1   Farner, D. S., "Circadian Systems in the Photoperiodic Responses of the Vertebrates." *Proc. Feldafing Summer School, September* 1964, *Circadian Clocks,* pp. 357–369. North-Holland Publ., Amsterdam, 1965   [4.8].

Far-2   Farner, D. S., "Predictive Functions in the Control of Annual Cycles." *Environ. Res.* **3**, 119–131 (1970)   [4.8].

Fel-1   Feldman, J. F., "Lengthening the Period of a Biological Clock in *Euglena* by Cycloheximide, an Inhibitor of Protein Synthesis." *Proc. Nat. Acad. Sci. U.S.* **57**, 1080–1087 (1967)   [3.3, 6.4, 6.6].

Fel-2   Feldman, J. F., "Circadian Rhytmicity in Amino Acid Incorporation in *Euglena gracillis.*" *Science* **160**, 1454–1456 (1968)   [2.4].

Fel-3   Feldman, J. F. and N. M. Waser, "New Mutations affecting Circadian Rhythmicity in *Neurospora,*" *Proc. Symp. Friday Harbor, Washington, September 1969, Biochronometry,* pp. 652–656. Nat. Acad. Sci., Washington, D. C., 1971   [2.2].

Fel-4   Feldman, J. F., M. N. Hoyle, and J. Shelgren, "Circadian Clock Mutants of *Neurospora crassa*: Genetic and Physiological Characteristics," *Genetics* (in press)   [4.3].

Fog-1   Fogel, M., and J. W. Hastings, "A Substrate-Binding Protein in the Conyaulax Bioluminescence Reaction." *Arch. Biochem. Biophys.* **142**, 310–321 (1971)   [2.4].

Fom-1   Fomin, S. V., "Some Mathematical Problems of Biology." *Biofizika* **15**, 344–351 (1970); *Biophysics (USSR)* **15**, 365–373 (1970)   [7.8].

Fre-1   Frenkel, R., "DPNH Oscillations in Glycolyzing Cell-Free Extracts from Beef Heart." *Biochem. Biophys. Res. Commun.* **21**, 497–502 (1965)   [2.5].

Frü-1   Fruhbeis, H., and A. Roder, "ESR-Undersuchungen an einem oszillierenden Redoxsystem." *Angew. Chem.* **10**, 208–209 (1971); *Angew. Chem. Int. Ed. Engl.* **10**, 192–193 (1971)   [2.5].

Gas-1   Gaston, S., and M. Menaker, "Pineal Function: The Biological Clock in the Sparrow?" *Science* **160**, 1125–1127 (1968)   [6.6].

Gas-2   Gaston, S., "The influence of the Pineal Organ on the Circadian Activity Rhythm in Birds." *Proc. Symp., Friday Harbor, Washington, September* 1969, *Biochronometry,* pp. 541–548. Nat. Acad. Sci., Washington, D.C., 1971   [6.6].

Gil-1   Gilpin, M. E., "Enriched Predator-Prey Systems: Theoretical Stability." *Science* **177**, 902–904 (1972)   [1.3].

God-1   Godfrey, M. D., H. Hoffman, R. Madden, C.S. Pittendrigh and S. Skopik,

195

"Data Analysis of Biological Time Series." *Life Sci. Space Res.* **8**, 215–233 (1970).

Goo-1   Goodwin, B. C., and M. H. Cohen, "A Phase-Shift Model for the Spatial and Temporal Organization of Developing Systems." *J. Theor. Biol.* **25**, 49–107 (1969) [8.8].

Gui-1   Guicking, A., "On the Effect of Sound on the Daily Periodic Activity of the Golden Hamster." *J. Interdiscpl. Cycle Res.* **1**, 323–334 (1970).

Gwi-1   Gwilliam, G. F., and J. C. Bradbury, "Activity Patterns in the Isolated Central Nervous System of the Barnacle and their Relation to Behavior." *Biol. Bull.* **141**, 502–513 (1971) [2.6].

Hal-1   Halaban, R., "The Circadian Rhythm of Leaf Movement of *Coleus blumei* × C. frederici, a Short Day Plant. I. Under Constant Light Conditions." *Plant Physiol.* **43**, 1883–1886 (1968).

Hal-2   Halaban, R., "The Circadian Rhythm of Leaf Movement of *Coleus blumei* × C. frederici, a Short Day Plant. II. The Effects of Light and Temperature Signals." *Plant Physiol.* **43**, 1887–1893 (1968).

Hal-3   Halaban, R., "The Flowering Response of *Coleus* in Relation to Photoperiod and the Circadian Rhythm of Leaf Movement." *Plant Physiol.* **43**, 1894–1898 (1968) [4.8].

Hal-4   Halaban, R., "Effects of Light Quality on the Circadian Rhythm of Leaf Movement of a Short-Day-Plant." *Plant Physiol.* **44**, 973–977 (1969) [3.3, 5.2].

Hal-5   Halaban, R., and W. S. Hillman, "Response of *Lemna persusilla* to Periodic Transfer to Distilled Water." *Plant Physiol.* **46**, 641–644 (1970) [6.6].

Halb-1   Halberg, F., "Temporal Coordination of Physiologic Function." *Cold Spring Harbor Symp. Quantitative Biol.*, 1960, *Biological Clocks*, **25**, pp. 289–310 (incl. discussion). Cold Spring Harbor Lab. Quant. Biol., Cold Spring Harbor, New York [2.2].

Halb-2   Halberg, F., "Chronobiologie: Rhythms et Physiologie Statistique." *Theoretical Physics and Biology*, pp. 347–393. North-Holland Publ., Amsterdam, 1969 [2.2].

Han-1   Hanson, F. E., J. F. Case, E. Buck, and J. Buck, "Synchrony and Flash Entrainment in a New Guinea Firefly." *Science* **174**, 161–164 (1971) [8.6, 8.8].

Har-1   Harmon, L. D., "Neuromimes: Action of a Reciprocally Inhibited Pair." *Science* **146**, 1323–1325 (1964) [2.6].

Har-2   Harmon, L. D., and E. R. Lewis, "Neural Modeling." *Physiol. Rev.* **46**, 513–591 (1966) [2.6].

Has-1   Hastings, J. W., "Unicellular Clocks." *Annu. Rev. Microbiol.* **13**, 297–312 (1959) [2.4, 6.6].

Has-2   Hastings, J. W., "Biochemical Aspects of Circadian Rhythms." *Cold Spring Harbor Symp. Quantitative Biol.*, 1960 *Biological Clocks*, **25**, pp. 131–143 (incl. discussion). Cold Spring Harbor Lab. Quant. Biol., Cold Spring Harbor, New York [2.2, 6.6].

Has-3   Hastings, J. W., and A. Keynan, "Molecular Aspects of Circadian Systems." *Proc. Feldafing Summer School, September* 1964, *Circadian Clocks*, pp. 167–182. North-Holland Publ., Amsterdam, 1965 [6.6].

Hau-1   Hauty, G. T., and T. Adams, "Phase Shifting of the Human Circadian System." *Proc. Feldafing Summer School, September* 1964, *Circadian Clocks*. pp, 413–425. North-Holland Publ., Amsterdam, 1965 [2.2].

Hep-1   Heppner, F. H., and D. S. Farner, "Periodicity in Self-Selection of Photoperiod." *Proc. Symp., Friday Harbor, Washington, September* 1969, *Biochronometry*, pp. 463–479. Nat. Acad. Sci., Washington, D.C., 1971 [4.8].

Hes-1   Hess, B., A. Boiteaux, and J. Krüger, "Cooperation of Glycolytic Enzymes." *Advan. Enzyme Regul.* **7**, 149–167 (1968)   [2.5].

Hig-1   Higgins, J., "A Chemical Mechanism for Oscillations of Glycolytic Intermediates in Yeast Cells." *Proc. Natl. Acad. Sci. U.S.* **51**, 989–994 (1964) [2.5].

Hig-2   Higgins, J., "The Theory of Oscillating Reactions." *Ind. Eng. Chem.* **59**, 18–62 (1967)   [2.5, 3.6, 8.3].

Hil-1   Hildebrant, G., "Spontaneous-Rhythmical Variations of Functional Capacity in Humans." *Med. Welt* **16**, 640–648 (1971) (in German)   [2.2].

Hof-1   Hoffman, K., "Versuche zur Analyse der Tagesperiodik. I. Der Einfluss der Lichtintesität." *Z. Vergl. Physiol.* **43**, 544–566 (1960)   [5.2].

Hof-2   Hoffmann, K., "Zur Beziehung Zwischen Phasenlage und Spontanfrequenz bei der Endogenen Tagesperiodik." *Z. Naturforsch.* **18**, 154–157 (1963)   [4.8].

Hof-3   Hoffmann, K., "Overt Circadian Frequencies and Circadian Rule." *Proc. Feldafing Summer School, September* 1964, *Circadian Clocks*, pp. 87–94. North-Holland Publ., Amsterdam, 1965   [5.2].

Hof-4   Hoffman, K., "Entrainment of the Circadian Rhythm of Locomotor Activity in Lizards by Temperature Cycles of Different Amplitude." *Z. Vergl. Physiol.* **58**, 225–228 (1968) (in German)   [4.3, 4.4, 4.8].

Hof-5   Hoffmann, K., "The Relative Effectiveness of Zeitgebers." *Oecologia* **3**, 184–206 (1969) (in German)   [4.8].

Hof-6   Hoffmann, K., "On the Influence of Strength of Zeitgeber on Phase in Synchronized Circadian Periodicities." *Z. Vergl. Physiol.* **62**, 93–110 (1969) (in German)   [4.3, 4.8].

Hof-7   Hoffmann, K., "Circadian Periodicity in Tree-Shrews (*Tupaia glis*) in Constant Conditions." *Zool. Ann. Suppl.* **33**, 171–177 (1969) (in German)   [8.2].

Hof-8   Hoffmann, K., "On Synchronization of Biological Rhythms." *Sonderdruck Verhandlungsber. Deut. Zool. Ges.* **64**, 266–273 (1970) (in German)   [4.8].

Hof-9   Hoffmann, K., "Biological Clocks in Animal Orientation and in Other Functions." *Proc. Int. Symp. Circadian Rhythmicity, Wegeningen*, 1971, pp. 175–205 [2.2].

Hof-10   Hoffmann, K., "Splitting of the Circadian Rhythm as a Function of Light Intensity." *Proc. Symp., Friday Harbor, Washington, September* 1969, *Biochronometry*, pp. 134–148. Nat. Acad. Sci., Washington D.C., 1971   [8.2].

Hös-1   Höser, N., "Phasenlage der Tagesperiodik von drei freibenden Vogelarten auf 51° nördlicher Breite in Abhängigkeit von der Jahreszeit." *Mauritanium* **7**, 49–58 (1971)   [4.8].

Hös-2   Höser, N., "Die intemen Phasenunterschiede in einem mit natürlichen Zeitgebem synchronisierten System circadianer Oscillatoren." *Mauritanium* **7**, 59–63 (1971)   [4.8].

Jac-1   Jacklet, J. W., "Circadian Rhythm of Optik Nerve Impulses Recorded in Darkness from Isolated Eye of *Aplysia*." *Science* **164**, 562–563 (1969)   [2.6].

Jac-2   Jacklet, J. W., "A Circadian Rhythm in Optic Nerve Impulses from an Isolated Eye in Darkness." *Proc. Symp., Friday Harbor, Washington, September* 1969, *Biochronometry*, pp. 351–362. Nat. Acad. Sci., Washington, D.C., 1971   [2.6].

Jac-3   Jacklet, J. W., and J. Geronimo, "Circadian Rhythm: Population of Interacting Neurons." *Science* **174**, 299–302 (1971)   [2.6, 8.5].

Jen-1   Jenks, R. D., "Quadratic Differential Systems for Interactive Population Models." *J. Differential Equations* **5**, 497–514 (1969)   [7.8].

Jer-1   Jerebzoff, S., "Manipulation of Some Oscillating Systems in Fungi by

Chemicals." *Proc. Feldafing Summer School, September* 1964, *Circadian Clocks*, pp. 183–189. North-Holland Publ., Amsterdam, 1965 [2.7, 6.6].

Joh-1 Johnsson, A., and H. G. Karlsson, "A Feedback Model for Biological Rhythms: I. Mathematical Description and Basic Properties of the Model." *J. Theor. Biol.* **36**, 153–174 (1972) [5.7].

Kar-1 Karakashian, M. W., and J. W. Hastings, "The Inhibition of a Biological Clock by Actinomycin D." *Proc. Nat. Acad. Sci. U.S.* **48**, 2130–2137 (1962) [6.6].

Kar-2 Karakashian, M. W., and J. W. Hastings, "The Effects of Inhibitors of Macromolecular Biosynthesis upon the Persistent Rhythm of Luminescence in *Gonyaulax.*" *J. Gen. Physiol.* **47**, 1–12 (1963) [6.6].

Karl-1 Karlsson, H. G., and A. Johnsson, "A Feedback Model for Biological Rhythms: II. Comparisons with Experimental Results, especially on the Petal Rhythm of *Kalanchoe.*" *J. Theor. Biol.* **36**, 175–194 (1972) [5.7].

Kel-1 Keller, E. F., "A Mathematical Description of Biological Clocks." *Curr. Mod. Biol.* **1**, 279–284 (1967) [5.7].

Kol-1 Koltermann, R., "Circadian Memory Rhythm After Scent and Color Training with Honey-Bees." *Z. Vergl. Physiol.* **75**, 49–68 (1971) [2.2].

Kon-1 Konopka, R. J., and S. Benzer, "Clock Mutants of *Drosophila melanogaster.*" *Proc. Nat. Acad. Sci. U.S.* **68**, 2112–2116 (1971) [2.2].

Kra-1 Kramm, K. R., "Circadian Activity in the Antelope Ground Squirrel *Ammospermophilus leucurus leucurus.*" *Ph.D. Thesis*, Dept. of Population and Environ. Biol., Univ. of California, Irvine, 1971 [4.8, 5.5, 8.2].

Lam-1 Lamprecht, G., and F. Weber, "The Entrainment of the Activity Periodicity of Species of the Genus *Carabus* by Zeitgebers of Different Frequencies." *Z. Vergl. Physiol.* **72**, 226–259 (1971) (in German) [4.4].

Lan-1 Langhaar, H. L., "General Population Theory in the Age-Time Continuum." *J. Franklin Inst.* **293**, 199–214 (1972) [1.3].

Lav-1 Lavenda, B., G. Nikolis, and M. Merschkovitz-Kaufman, "Chemical Instabilities and Relaxation Oscillations." *J. Theor. Biol.* **39**, 283–292 (1971) [2.5, 8.4, 8.8].

Lef-1 Lefever, R., G. Nikolis, and I. Prigogine, "On the Occurence of Oscillations Around the Steady State in Systems of Chemical Reactions far from Equilibrium." *J. Chem. Phys.* **47**, 1045–1047 (1967) [2.5, 8.8].

Lef-2 Lefever, R., "Dissipative Structures in Chemical Systems." *J. Chem. Phys.* **49**, 4977–4978 (1968) [2.5, 8.4, 8.8].

Lef-3 Lefever, R., and G. Nikolis, "Chemical Instabilities and Sustained Oscillations." *J. Theor. Biol.* **30**, 267–284 (1971) [2.5, 8.8].

Mac-1 MacArthur, R. H., "Ecological Consequences of Natural Selection." *In Theoretical and Mathematical Biology* (H. S. Morovitz and T. H. Waterman, eds.), pp. 388–397. Ginn (Blaisdell), Boston, Massachusetts [1.3].

McC-1 McCluskey, E. S., "Recent Reports on Circadian Rhythms in Man." *Med. Arts Sci.* **3**, 4, 45–64 (1970) [2.2].

McM-1 McMurry, L., and J. W. Hastings, "No Desynchronization Among Four Circadian Rhythms in the Unicellular Alga, *Gonyaulax polyedra.*" *Science* **175**, 1137–1139 (1972) [2.2, 2.4].

Mar-1 Markowitz, D., "Co-operativity Model of Cellular Control: Organization and Complexity." *J. Theor. Biol.* **35**, 27–53 (1972).

Mat-1 Mathieu, P. A., and F. A. Roberge, "Characteristics of Pacemaker Oscillations in *Aplysia* Neurons." *Can. J. Physiol. Pharmacal* **49**, 787–795 (1971) [2.6].

198

May-1 May, R. M., "Limit Cycles in Predator-Prey Communities." *Science* **177**, 900–902 (1972) [1.3].

Men-1 Menaker, M., "Circadian Rhythms and Photoperiodism in *Passer domesticus.*" *Proc. Feldafing Summer School, September* 1964, *Circadian Clocks*, pp. 385–395. North-Holland Publ., Amsterdam, 1965 [4.8].

Men-2 Menaker, M., and H. Heats, "Extraretinal Light Perception in the Sparrow, II. Photoperiodic Stimulation of Testis Growth." *Proc. Nat. Acad. Sci. U.S.* **60**, 146–151 (1968) [6.6].

Men-3 Menaker, M., "Biological Clocks." *BioScience* **19**, 681–689 (1969) [2.2].

Men-4 Menaker, M., "Synchronization with the Photic Environment via Extraretinal Receptors in the Avian Brain." *Proc. Symp., Friday Harbor, Washington, September* 1969, *Biochronometry*, pp. 315–332. Nat. Acad. Sci., Washington, D.C., 1971 [6.6].

Mend-1 Mendelson, M., "Oscillator Neurons in Crustacean Ganglia." *Science* **171**, 1170–1173 (1971) [2.6].

Min-1 Minis, D. H., "Parallel Peculiarities in the Entrainment of a Circadian Rhythm and Photoperiodic Induction in the Pink Boll Worm (*Pectinophora gossypiella.*" *Proc. Feldafing Summer School, September* 1964, *Circadian Clocks*, pp. 333–343. North-Holland Publ., Amsterdam, 1965 [4.8].

Min-2 Minis, D. H., and C. S. Pittendrigh, "Circadian Oscillation Controlling Hatching: Its Ontogemy During Embryogenesis of a Moth." *Science* **159**, 534–536 (1968).

Mol-1 Molchanov, A. M., "Endogenous Biochemical Oscillations as the Probable Basis of Physiological Rhythms." *Biofizika* **16**, 878–883 (1971) (in Russian) [5.7].

Mos-1 Moser, J., "On the Theory of Quasi-periodic Motions." *SIAM (Soc. Ind. Appl. Math.) Rev.* **8**, 145–172 (1966) [1.4, 7.8].

Mur-1 Murakami, H., "Rhythm of the Water Intake of Rodents in the Continuous Illumination." *Anim (Tokyo)* **20**, 29–32 (1971) (in Japanese) [2.2].

Nat-1 Natalini, J. J., "Relationship of the Phase-Response Curve for Light to the Free-Running Period of the Kangaroo Rat, *Dipodomys merriami.*" *Physiol. Zool.* **45**, 153–166 (1972) [5.5].

Nis-1 Nishiitsutsuji-Uwo, J., S. F. Petropulos, and C. S. Pittendrigh, "Central Nervous System Control of Circadian Rhythmycity in the Cockroach. I. Role of the Pars Intercerebralis." *Biol. Bull.* **133**, 679–696 (1967) [6.6].

Nis-2 Nishiitsutsuji-Uwo, J., and C. S. Pittendrigh, "Central Nervous System Control of Circadian Rhythmicity in the Cockroach. II. The Pathway of Light Signals that Entrain the Rhythm." *Z. Vergl. Physiol.* **58**, 1–13 (1968) [6.6].

Nis-3 Nishiitsutsuji-Uwo, J., and C. S. Pittendrigh, "Central Nervous System Control of Circadian Rhythmicity in the Cockroach. III. The Optic Lobes, Locus of the Driving Oscillations ?" *Z. Vergl. Physiol.* **58**, 14–46 (1968) [6.6].

Oth-1 Othmer, H. G., and L. E. Scriven, "Instability and Dynamic Pattern in Cellular Networks." *J. Theor. Biol.* **32**, 507–537 (1971) [8.4].

Ott-1 Ottesen, E. A., "Analytical Studies on a Model for the Entrainment of Circadian Systems." *B.A. Thesis*, Dept. of Biol., Princeton Univ. Princeton, New Jersey, 1965 [3.7, 4.5, 4.6].

Pac-1 Packer, L., K. Utsumi, and M. G. Mustafa, "Oscillatory States of Mitochondria. I. Electron and Energy Transfer Pathways." *Arch. Biochem. Biophys.* **117**, 381–393 (1966) [2.5].

Pag-1 Page, C. H., and D. M. Wilson, "Unit Responses in the Metathoracic Ganglion of the Flying Locust." *Fed. Proc. Fed. Amer. Soc. Exp. Biol.* **29**, 590 (1970) [2.6].

Pan-1   Pannella, G., "Fish Otoliths: Daily Growth Layers and Periodical Patterns." *Science* **173**, 1124–1127 (1971)   [2.2].

Pav-1   Pavlidis, T., "A New Model for Simple Neural Nets and its Application in the Design of a Neural Oscillator." *Bull. Math. Biophys.* **27**, 215–229 (1965)   [2.6].

Pav-2   Pavlidis, T., "Design of Neural Nets with Intermittent Response and Certain Other Relevant Studies." *Bull. Math. Biophys.* **28**, 51–74 (1966)   [2.6].

Pav-3   Pavlidis, T., "A Mathematical Model for the Light Affected System in the Drosophila Eclosion Rhythm." *Bull. Math. Biophys.* **29**, 291–310 (1967)   [3.7, 4.5].

Pav-4   Pavlidis, T., "A Model for Circadian Clocks." *Bull. Math. Biophys.* **29**, 781–791 (1967)   [5.3, 5.4, 5.5, 5.7].

Pav-5   Pavlidis, T., "Studies on Biological Clocks: A Model for the Circadian Rhythms of Nocturnal Organisms." *In Lectures on Mathematics in Life Sciences* (M. Gerstenhaber, ed), pp. 88–112. Amer. Math. Soc., Providence, Rhode Island, 1968   [5.3, 5.4, 5.5, 5.7].

Pav-6   Pavlidis, T., W. F. Zimmerman, and J. Osborn, "A Mathematical Model for the Temperature Effects on Circadian Rhythms." *J. Theor. Biol.* **18**, 210–221 (1968)   [6.3].

Pav-7   Pavlidis, T., "An Explanation of the Oscillatory Free-Runs in Circadian Rhythms." *Amer. Natur.* **103**, 31–42 (1969)   [4.4, 5.5].

Pav-8   Pavlidis, T., "Populations of Interacting Oscillators and Circadian Rhythms." *J. Theor. Biol.* **22**, 418–436 (1969)   [7.5, 7.8, 8.8].

Pav-9   Pavlidis, T., and W. Kauzmann, "Toward a Quantitative Biochemical Model for Circadian Oscillators." *Arch. Biochem. Biophys.* **132**, 338–348 (1969)   [3.6, 5.2, 6.3, 8.3].

Pav-10   Pavlidis, T., "Mathematical Models of Circadian Rhythms: Their Usefulness and Their Limitations." *Proc. Symp., Friday Harbor, Washington, September 1969, Biochronometry*, pp. 110–116. Nat. Acad. Sci., Washington, D.C., 1971 [5.7, 6.6].

Pav-11   Pavlidis, T., "Populations of Biochemical Oscillators as Circadian Clocks." *J. Theor. Biol.* **33**, 319–338 (1971)   [7.6, 7.8, 8.3, 8.8].

Pav-12   Pavlidis, T., "The Existence of Synchronous States in Populations of Oscillators." *In Quanti. Biol. of Metabolism* (A. Locker, ed.), pp. 73–80. Springer-Verlag, Berlin and New York, 1973   [7.6, 7.8, 8.4, 8.8].

Pie-1   Pierce, J. R., "Synchronizing Digital Networks." *Bell Syst. Tech. J.*, **48**, 615–636 (1969)   [7.8].

Pit-1   Pittendrigh, C. S., and V. C. Bruce, "An Oscillator Model for Biological Clocks." *In Rhythmic and Synthetic Processes in Growth* (D. Rudnick, ed.), pp. 75–109. Princeton Univ. Press, Princeton, New Jersey, 1957   [5.7, 8.1].

Pit-2   Pittendrigh, C. S., "Daily Rhythms as Coupled Oscillator Systems and their Relation to Thermoperiodism and Photoperiodism." *Photoperiodism and Related Phenomena in Plants and Animals*, pp. 475–505. Amer. Assoc. Advan. Sci., Washington, D.C., 1959   [4.8, 5.7, 8.1].

Pit-3   Pittendrigh, C. S., "Circadian Rhythms and the Circadian Organization of Living Systems." *Cold Spring Harbor Symp. Quantitative Biol.*, 1960, *Biological Clocks*, **25**, pp. 159–184. Cold Spring Harbor Lab. Quant. Biol., Cold Spring Harbor, New York   [2.2, 3.3, 3.7, 5.7, 8.1, 8.2].

Pit-4   Pittendrigh, C. S., "On Temporal Organization in Living Systems." *Harvey Lect.* **56**, 93–125 (1961)   [2.2, 2.3, 3.7].

Pit-5   Pittendrigh, C. S., and D. H. Minis, "The Entrainment of Circadian Oscillations by Light and Their Role as Photoperiodic Clocks." *Amer. Natur.* **98**, 261–294 (1964) [3.3, 3.7, 4.5, 4.6, 4.8].

Pit-6   Pittendrigh, C. S., "On the Mechanism of the Entrainment of a Circadian Rhythm by Light Cycles." *Proc. Feldafing Summer School, September* 1964, *Circadian Clocks*, pp. 277–297. North-Holland Publ., Amsterdam, 1965 [3.7, 4.5, 4.6].

Pit-7   Pittendrigh, C. S., "The Circadian Oscillation in *Drosophila pseudoobscura* pupae: A Model for the Photoperiodic Clock." *Z. Pflanzenphysiol.* **54**, 275–307 (1966) [2.3, 3.7, 4.5, 4.6].

Pit-8   Pittendrigh, C. S., "Circadian Systems, I. The Driving Oscillation and its Assay in *Drosophila pseudoobscura.*" *Proc. Nat. Acad. Sci. U.S.* **58**, 1762–1767 (1967) [2.2, 2.3].

Pit-9   Pittendrigh, C. S., "Circadian Rhythms, Space Research and Manned Space Flight." *Life Sci. Space Res.* **5**, 122–134 (1967) [8.2, 8.7].

Pit-10   Pittendrigh, C. S., and S. D. Skopik, "Circadian Systems, V. The Driving Oscillation and the Temporal Sequence of Development." *Proc. Nat. Acad. Sci. U.S.* **65**, 500–507 (1970) [2.3].

Pit-11   Pittendrigh, C. S., and D. H. Minis, "The Photoperiodic Time Measurement in *Pectinophera gossypiella* and its Relation to the Circadian System in that Species." *Proc. Symp., Friday Harbor, Washington, September* 1969, *Biochronometry*, pp. 212–250. Nat. Acad. Sci., Washington, D.C., 1971 [4.8].

Pit-12   Pittendigh, C. S., J. H. Eichhom, D. H. Minis, and V. G. Bruce, "Circadian Systems: VI. Photoperiodic Time Measurement in *Pectinophera gossypiella.*" *Proc. Nat. Acad. Sci. U.S.* **66**, 758–764 (1970) [4.8].

Pos-1   Posin, N. U., and Yu. A. Shulpin, "The Analysis of the Work of Autooscillative Neuron Combinations." *Biofizika* **15**, 156–163 (1970) (in Russian) [2.6].

Pri-1   Prigogine, I., and G. Nikolis, "On Symmetry-Breaking Instabilities in Dissipative Systems." *J. Chem. Phys.* **46**, 3542–3550 (1967) [2.5, 8.8].

Pri-2   Prigogine, I., *Introduction to Irreversible Processes*, 3rd ed., Wiley, New York, 1968 [2.5].

Pri-3   Prigogine, I., and R. Lefever, "Symmetry Breaking Instabilities in Dissipative Systems. II." *J. Chem. Phys.* **48**, 1695–1700 (1968) [2.5].

Pri-4   Prigogine, I., "Structure, Dissipation and Life." *In Theoretical Physics and Biology* (M. Marois, ed.), pp. 23–52. North-Holland Publ., Amsterdam, 1969 [2.5, 8.8].

Pri-5   Prigogine, I., R. Lefever, A. Goldbeter and, M. Hersch Kowitz-Kaufman, "Symmetry Breaking Instabilities in Biological Systems." *Nature (London)* **223**, 913–916 (1969) [2.5, 8.8].

Pri-6   Prigogine, I., and G. Nikolis, "Biological Order, Srtucture and Instabilities," [2.5, 8.8].

Pye-1   Pye, K., and B. Chance, "Sustained Sinusoidal Oscillations of Reduced Pyridine Nucleotide in a Cell-Free Extract of Saccharomyces Carlsbergensis." *Proc. Nat. Acad. Sci.* **55**, 888–894 (1966) [2.5, 4.4].

Pye-2   Pye, K., and B. Chance, "Sustained Sinosoidal Oscillations of Reduced Pyridine Nucleotide in a Cell-Free Extract of Saccharomyces Carlsbergensis." *Proc. Nat. Acad. Sci. U.S.* **55** 888–894 (1966) [2.5].

Pye-3   Pye, E. K., "Biochemical Mechanisms Underlying the Metabolic Oscillations in Yeast." *Can. J. Bot.* **47**, 271–285 (1969) [2.5].

Pye-4   Pye, E. K., "Periodicities in Intermediary Metabolism." *Proc. Symp., Friday Harbor, Washington, September* 1969, *Biochronometry*, pp. 623–636. Nat. Acad. Sci., Washington, D.C., 1971 [2.5, 3.3].

Ren-1   Rensing, L., "Hormonal Control of Circadian Rhythms in *Drosophila*."
         Proc. Symp., Friday Harbor, Washington, September 1969, *Biochronometry*,
         pp. 527–540. Nat. Acad. Sci., Washington, D.C., 1971.
Ric-1   Richter, C. P., "Inborn Nature of The Rat's 24-hour Clock." *J. Comp. Physiol.
         Psych.* **75**, 1–4 (1971)   [2.2].
Rob-1   Roberts, S. K. F., "Circadian Activity in Cockroaches. I. The Free-Running
         Rhythm in Steady State." *J. Cell. Comp. Physiol.* **55**, 99–110 (1960)   [5.2, 8.2].
Rob-2   Roberts, S. K. F., "Circadian Activity Rhythms in Cockroaches: II. Entrain-
         ment and Phase Shifting." *J. Cell. Comp. Physiol.* **59**, 175–196 (1962)   [4.7, 4.8].
Rob-3   Roberts, S. K. F., "Significance of Endocrines and Central Nervous System in
         Circadian Rhythms." *Proc. Feldafing Summer School, September* 1964, *Circadian
         Clocks*, pp. 198–213. North-Holland Publ., Amsterdam, 1965   [6.6].
Rob-4   Roberts, S. K. F., "Circadian Activity in Cockroaches. III. The Role of Endo-
         crine and Neural Factors." *J. Cell. Physiol.* **67**, 473–486 (1966)   [6.6].
Rob-5   Roberts, S. K., S. D. Skopik, and R. J. Driskill, "Circadian Rhythms in
         Cockroaches: Does Brain Hormone Mediate the Locomotor Cycle." *Proc.
         Symp., Friday Harbor, Washington, September* 1969, *Biochronometry*, pp. 505–
         516. Nat. Acad. Sci., Washington, D. C., 1971 [6.6].
Ros-1   Rosenwing, M., and R. H. MacArthur, "Graphical Representation and Stability
         Conditions of Predator-Prey Interactions." *Amer. Natur.* **97**, 209–223 (1971)
         [1.3].
Ros-2   Rosenweig, M. L., Discussion. *Science* **177**, 904 (1972)   [1.3].
San-1   Sandberg, I. W., "On Conditions Under Which it is Possible to Synchronize
         Digital Transmission Systems." *Bell Syst. Tech. J.* **48**, 1999–2022 (1969)
         [4.8, 7.8].
San-2   Sandberg, I. W., "Some Properties of a Nonlinear Model of a System for
         Synchronizing Digital Transmission Networks." [7.8].
Sau-1   Saunders, D. S., "Circadian Clock in Insect Photoperiodism." *Science* **168**,
         601–603 (1970)   [4.8].
See-1   Seeling, F. F., "Undamped Sinusoidal Oscillations in Linear Chemical Reaction
         Systems". *J. Theor. Biol.* **27**, 197–206 (1970)   [2.5].
See-2   Seeling, F. F., and F. Gröbber, "Stable Linear Reaction Oscillation." *J. Theor.
         Biol.* **30**, 485–496 (1971)   [2.5].
See-3   Seeling, F. F., "Activated Enzyme Catalysis as a Possible Realization of the
         Stable Linear Chemical Oscillator Model." *J. Theor. Biol.* **30**, 497–514 (1971)
         [2.5].
Sel-1   Selkov, E. E., "Oscillations in Biochemical Systems, Experimental Data,
         Hypotheses, Models." *In Oscillatory Processes in Biological and Chemical
         Systems* (A.M. Frank *et al.*, eds.), pp. 7–22. Nauka, Moscow, 1967 (in Russian)
         [2.5].
Sel-2   Selkov, E. E., "Investigation of the Conditions for the Appearance of Periodic
         Oscillations in Systems and Forms of Coherence." *Oscillatory Processes in
         Biological and Chemical Systems* (A.M. Frank *et al.*, eds.), pp. 81–93. Nauka,
         Moscow, 1967 (in Russian)   [2.5].
Sel-3   Selkov, E. E., "On the Possibility of Appearance of Self Oscillations in Fermenta-
         tion Reactions and Compression of Substrates and Products." In *Oscillatory
         Processes in Biological and Chemical Systems* (A.M. Frank *et al.*, eds.), pp. 93–113.
         Nauka, Moscow, 1967 (in Russian)   [2.5].
Sel-4   Selkov, E. E., "Self-Oscillations in Glycolysis. 1. A Simple Kinetic Model."
         Eur. J. Biochem. **4**, 79–86 (1968)   [2.5].

Sel-5   Selkov, E. E., "The Alternative Auto-oscillating Stationary States in Thiole Metabolism—Two Alternative Types of Cell Reproduction: Normal and Malignant." *Biofizika* **15**, 1065–1073 (1970); *Biophysics (USSR)* **15**, 1104–1112 (1970) [2.5, 8.2].

Sko-1   Skopik, S. D., and C. S. Pittendrigh, "Circadian Systems, II. The Oscillation in the Individual Drosophila Pupa; Its Independence of Developmental Stage." *Proc. Nat. Acad. Sci. U.S.* **58**, 1862–1869 (1967).

Ste-1   Stebel, J., and R. Sinz, "On Central Nervous Minute-Periodicity and Its Coordination." *J. Interdiscipl. Cycle Res.* **2**, 63–72 (1971) [2.6].

Str-1   Strumwasser, F., "The Demonstration and Manipulation of a Circadian Rhythm in a Single Neuron." *Proc. Feldafing Summer School, September* 1964, *Circadian Clocks*, pp. 442–462. North-Holland, Publ., Amsterdam, 1965 [2.2, 2.6].

Sut-1   Suter, R. B., and K. S. Rawson, "Circadian Activity Rhythm of the Dear Mouse, Peromyscus: effect of Deuterium Oxide." *Science* **160**, 1011–1014 (1968) [6.5].

Swa-1   Swade, R. H., "Circadian Rhythms in the Arctic." *Ph.D. Thesis*, Dept. of Biol., Princeton Univ., Princeton, New Jersey, 1963 [4.4, 8.2].

Swa-2   Swade, R. H., and C. S., Pittendrigh "Circadian Locomotor Rhythms of Rodents in the Arctic." *Amer. Natur.* **101**, 431–466 (1967) [4.3, 4.4].

Swa-3   Swade, R. H., "Circadian Rhythms in Fluctuating Light Cycles: Toward a New Model of Entrainment." *J. Theoret. Biol.* **24**, 227–239 (1969) [4.4].

Swa-4   Swade, R. H., "A Split Activity Rhythm Under Fluctuating Light Cycles." *Proc. Symp., Friday Harbor, Washington, September* 1969, *Biochronometry*, pp. 148–149. Nat. Acad. Sci., Washington, D.C., 1971 [8.2].

Swe-1   Sweeney, B. M., and J. W. Hastings, "Effects of Temperature on Diurnal Rhythms." *Cold Spring Harbor Symp. Quantitative Biol.*, 1960, *Biological Clocks*, **25**, pp. 87–104. Cold Spring Harbor Lab. Quant. Biol., Cold Spring Harbor, New York [6.3].

Swe-2   Sweeney, B., "Biological Clocks in Plants." *Annu. Rev. Plant Physiol.* **14**, 411–440 (1963) [2.2].

Swe-3   Sweeney, B. M., "Rhythmicity in the Biochemistry of Photosynthesis in *Gonvaulax*." *Proc. Feldafing Summer School, September* 1964, *Circadian Clocks*, pp. 190–194. North-Holland Publ., Amsterdam, 1965 [6.6].

Swe-4   Sweeney, B., "Transducing Mechanism Between Circadian Clock and Overt Rhythms in *Gonvaulax*." *Can. J. Bot.* **47**, 299–309 (1969) [6.6].

Und-1   Underwood, H., and M. Menaker, "Photoperiodically Significant Photoreception in Sparrows: Is the Retina Involved?" *Science* **167**, 298–301 (1970) [4.8].

Uts-1   Utsumi, K., and L. Packer, "Oscillatory States of Mitochondria. II. Factors Controlling Period and Amplitude." *Arch. Biochem. Biophys.* **120**, 401–412 (1967) [2.5].

Van-1   Vanden Driessche T., "Possible Diversity in Basic Mechanisms of Biological Oscillations." *J. Interdiscipl. Cycle Res.* **2**, 133–145 (1971) [2.2, 6.6].

Van-2   Vanden Driessche, T., "Circadian Rhythms in Whole and in Anucleate *Acetabularia*." *Gegenbaurs Morphol. Jahrb., Leipzig* **117**, 81–83 (1971) [6.6].

Van-3   Vanden Driessche, T., "Structural and Functional Rhythms in the Chloroplasts of *Acetabularia*: Molecular Aspects of the Circadian System." *Proc. Symp., Friday Harbor, Washington, September* 1969, *Biochronometry*, pp. 612–622. Nat. Acad. Sci., Washington, D.C., 1971 [6.6.].

van G-1   van Gooch, D., and L. Packer, "Adenine Nuclootide Control of Heart Mitochondrial Oscillations." *Biochim. Biophys. Acta* **245**, 17–20 (1971) [2.5].

von B-1 von Bodman, K., "The Effect of Drugs on the Estimation of Short Time Intervals and the Circadian Rhythm of Mammals." *Z. Vergl. Physiol.* **68**, 276–292 (1970) [2.2].

Wal-1 Walter, C. F., "The Occurence and the Significance of Limit Cycle Behavior in Controlled Biochemical Systems." *J. Theor. Biol.* **27**, 259–272 (1970) [2.5, 7.8].

Wev-1 Wever, R., "Zum Mechanismus der biologischen 24-Stunden-Periodik." *Kybemetik* **1**, 139–154 (1962) [5.3, 5.7].

Wev-2 Wever, R., "Zum Mechanismus der Biologischen 24-Stunden-Periodik. II. Der Einfluss des Gleichwertes auf die Eigenschaften Selbsterregter Schwingungen." *Kybemetik* **1**, 213–231 (1963) [5.3, 5.7, 8.2].

Wev-3 Wever, R., "Zum Mechanismus der Biologischen 24–Stunden-Periodik. III. Anwendung der Modell-Gleichung." *Kybemetik* **2**, 127–144 (1964) [4.8, 5.7].

Wev-4 Wever, R., "A Mathematical Model for Circadian Rhythms." *Proc. Feldafing Summer School, September 1964, Circadian Clocks*, pp. 47–63. North-Holland Publ., Amsterdam, 1965 [4.8, 5.3, 5.7].

Wev-5 Wever, R., "The Influence of Twilight on Circadian Rhythms." *Z. Vergl. Physiol.* **55**, 255–277 (1967) [5.7].

Wilk-1 Wilkins, M. B., "The Influence of Temperature and Temperature Changes on Biological Clocks." *Proc. Feldafing Summer School, September 1964, Circadian Clocks*, pp. 146–163. North-Holland Publ., Amsterdam, 1965 [6.3].

Will-1 Wille, J. J., and C. F. Ehret, "Light Synchronization of an Endogenous Circadian Rhythm of Cell Division in *Tetrahymena*." *J. Protozool.* **15**, 785–788 (1968) [2.4].

Will-2 Wille, J. J., and C. F. Ehret, "Circadian Rhythm of Pattern Formation in Populations of a Free-Swimming Organism, *Tetrahymena*." *J. Protozool.* **15**, 789–792 (1968) [2.4].

Wils-1 Wilson, D. M., "The Central Nervous Control of Flight in a Locust." *J. Exp. Biol.*, **38** 471–490 (1961) [2.6].

Wils-2 Wilson, D. M., and T. Weis-Fogh, "Patterned Activity of Co-ordinated Motor Units, Studied in Flying Locusts." *J. Exp. Biol.* **39**, 643–667 (1962) [2.6].

Wils-3 Wilson, D. M., "Inherent Asymmetry and Reflex Modulation of the Locust Flight Motor Pattern." *J. Exp. Biol.* **48**, 631–641 (1968) [2.8].

Wils-4 Wilson, D. M., "Genetic and Sensory Mechanisms for Locomotion and Orientation in Animals." *Amer. Sci.* **60**, 358–365 (1972) [2.6].

Win-0 Winfree, A. T., "Biological Rhythms and the Behavior of Populations of Coupled Oscillators." *J. Theor. Biol.* **16**, 15–42 (1967) [7.8, 8.8].

Win-1 Winfree, A. T., "The Effect of Light Flashes on a Circadian Rhythm in *Drosophila pseudoobscura*." *Ph. D.Thesis*, Dept. of Biol., Princeton Univ., Princeton, New Jersey, 1970 [5.6].

Win-2 Winfree, A. T., "The Temporal Morphology of a Biological Clock." *In Lectures on Mathematics in the Life Sciences* (M. Gerstenhaber, ed.), Vol. 2, pp. 111–150. Amer. Math. Soc., Providence, Rhode Island, 1970 [3.2, 3.7].

Win-3 Winfree, A. T., "Integrated View of Resetting a Circadian Clock." *J. Theor. Biol.* **28**, 327–374 (1970) [2.3, 3.2, 3.3, 3.7, 5.6].

Win-4 Winfree, A. T., "The Oscillatory Control of Cell Differentiation in Nectria." *Proc. IEEE* Symp. Adoptive Process. Decision and Control, 1970, Vols. XXIII. 4.1-XXIII. 4.5 [8.4].

Win-5 Winfree, A. T., "Corkscrews and Singularities in Fruitflies: Resetting Behavior of the Circadian Eclosion Rhythm." *Proc. Symp., Friday Harbor, Washington,*

September 1969, *Biochronometry*, pp. 81–109. Nat. Acad. Sci., Washington, D.C., 1971 [5.6].

Win-6   Winfree, A. T., "Spiral Waves of Chemical Activity." *Science* **175**, 634–635 (1972) [8.4, 8.8].

Win-7   Winfree, A. T., "Acute Temperature Sensitivity of the Circadian Rhythm in *Drosophila*." *J. Insect. Physiol.* **18**, 181–185 (1972) [5.6, 6.3].

Win-8   Winfree, A. T., "On the Photosensitivity of the Circadian Time-Sense in *Drosophila pseudoobscura*." *J. Theor. Biol.* **35**, 159–189 (1972).

Win-9   Winfree, A. T., "Oscillatory Glycolysis in Yeast: The Pattern of Phase Resetting by Oxygen." *Arch. Biochem. Biophys.* **149**, 88–401 (1972).

Zai-1   Zaikin, A. N., and A. M. Zhabotinsky, "Concentration Wave Propagation in Two-dimensional Liquid-phase Self-Oscillating System." *Nature (London)* **225**, 535–537 (1970) [2.5, 8.4].

Zha-1   Zhabotinski, A. M., "Periodic Course of Oxidation of Malonic Acid in Solution (Investigation of the Kinetics of the Reaction of Belousor)." *Biophysics* **9**, 329–335 1964; or *Biofizika*, **9**, 306–311 (1964) [2.5].

Zha-2   Zhadin, M. N., "Mechanisms of Origin of Synchronization of the Biopotentials of the Cerebral Cortex-II. Model of Dependent Sources." *Biophysics* **14**, 944–952 (1969); *Biofizika* **14**, 897–904 (1969) [8.8].

Zim-1   Zimmerman, W. F., " The Effects of Temperature on the Circadian Rhythm of Eclosion in *Drosophila pseudoobscura*." *Ph.D. Thesis*, Dept. of Biol., Princeton Univ., Princeton, New Jersey, 1966 [5.3, 6.3].

Zim-2   Zimmerman, W. F., C. S. Pittendrigh, and T. Pavlidis, "Temperature Compensation of the Circadian Oscillation in *Drosophila pseudoobscura* and its Entrainment by Temperature Cycles." *J. Insect. Physiol.* **14**, 669–684 (1968) [3.7, 5.2, 6.3].

Zim-3   Zimmerman, W. F., "On the Absense of Circadian Rhythmicity in *Drosophila pseudoobscura* Pupae." *Biol. Bull.* **136**, 494–500 (1969) [5.6].

Zim-4   Zimmerman, W. F., and D. Ives, "Some Photophysiological Aspects of Circadian Rhythmicity in *Drosophila*." *Proc. Symp., Friday Harbor, Washington, September* 1969, *Biochronometry*, pp. 381–391. Nat. Acad. Sci., Washington, D.C., 1971.

Zim-5   Zimmerman, W. F., and T. H. Goldsmith, "Photosensitivity of the Circadian Rhythm and of Visual Receptors in Carotenoid-Depleted *Drosophila*." *Science* **171**, 1167–1169 (1971).

Index

205